ATLAS OF THE HUMAN BRAIN IN SECTION

ATLAS
OF
THE HUMAN BRAIN
IN SECTION

Melville Roberts, B.S., M.D., F.A.C.S.

Chairman, Division of Neurosurgery
Associate Professor of Surgery
University of Connecticut School of Medicine
Hartford, Connecticut

Joseph Hanaway, A.B., M.D.

Assistant Professor of Anatomy
University of Virginia School of Medicine
Charlottesville, Virginia

LEA & FEBIGER · PHILADELPHIA

Reprinted July, 1971

ISBN 0-8121-0261-4

Published in Great Britain by
Henry Kimpton, Publishers

Library of Congress Catalog Card Number: 75-98494
PRINTED IN THE UNITED STATES OF AMERICA

CONTENTS

INTRODUCTION

Purpose

This atlas has been designed to aid in the study of the cross-sectional anatomy of the human brain. The stimulus for this work came from the authors' discovery that none of the available atlases depicted stained whole serial sections in three planes. Although unstained specimens have the advantage of appearing natural, many structures are difficult to see because of insufficient contrast between white and gray matter. By staining the gray matter of whole sections (Roberts and Hanaway, 1969), we have been able to increase contrast without destroying the resemblance to unaltered brain.

Photographs rather than drawings have been used. In the interest of clarity, drawings allow emphasis of some structures or omission of others, but nevertheless represent an artist's conception rather than the specimen itself. Although photographs afford realism that may be lost in an artist's interpretation, they also have disadvantages. One obvious drawback of photographs is that they reveal with equal accuracy imperfections and artefacts. Utmost care, therefore, has been taken in preparing the slices used for this atlas, and in most cases major defects have been avoided.

Preparation of Brain Slices

Many techniques have been described for staining whole brain slices to facilitate macroscopic study. We found that the most satisfactory results were produced by modifying a technique that precipitated copper in gray matter (Mulligan, 1931), imparting a red-brown color while leaving white matter unstained. For those who may want to prepare similar sections the technique is given here in detail:

Fixation: As soon as the brain has been removed, the vertebral and internal carotid arteries are each perfused with 50 ml of 40% formalin. The brain is then placed in 10% formalin, suspended on string by the basilar artery to prevent deformity, and kept in this solution for 2 to 4 weeks to permit fixation. If the fixation period is for less than 2 weeks, slicing will be faulty because the white matter will still be relatively soft. Fixation for longer than 6 weeks may result in uneven staining. Poor staining also occurs if the brain has not been removed promptly following death or if it is from a patient who suffered significant periods of anoxia prior to death. Brains that are cleared of blood by thorough perfusion usually stain better than those that have been only partially cleared.

Sectioning: The fixed brain is serially sliced into 4-mm sections on a Hobart Model, 410 rotary-blade, electrically driven commercial meat slicer. This slicer produces symmetric sections of uniform thickness virtually free of knife marks. Embedding the brain in agar does not facilitate cutting; in some specimens the agar leaves an unsightly rim about gyri and in sulci. Slices less than 4 mm thick tend to fragment and curl during staining, and are generally difficult to handle. Handling is facilitated by stacking the sections between sheets of wet filter paper that can be used to carry them to the first washing bath. To make coronal slices symmetric, prior to machine sectioning an initial cut is made with a brain knife immediately anterior to the temporal poles. Symmetric horizontal sections are made after a plane has been established by hand-cutting above the corpus callosum. Horizontal sections are the most difficult to keep symmetric and to hold together, especially at the base of the brain. Sagittal sections are cut in a medial to lateral direction from a bisected brain.

Staining: After cutting, the stacked slices are washed in running tap water for 30 minutes. If the meninges are to be removed, this should be done prior to staining; if they are removed afterwards, patches of unstained cortex will be exposed. With the copper sulfate-phenol-ferrocyanide technique the meninges are only lightly stained and removal is unnecessary. Pia-arachnoid and related blood vessels are thus well demonstrated. After washing, each slice is immersed for 6 minutes at 60°C in not less than 1.5 liters of a solution containing: $CuSO_4 . 5H_2O$, 5 gm; phenol, 50 gm; HCl (conc.), 1 ml; and distilled water, 1000 ml. (A deep Pyrex dish is convenient for use in this step.) If a smaller amount is used, the solution becomes exhausted quickly and poor staining results. When the solution starts to become cloudy it should be discarded, usually after one half of an adult brain has been stained. The white matter is protected from staining by a fatty film formed by the action of phenol on myelin (Kampmeier and Hodspodar, 1951). If the copper sulfate-phenol solution is cool or if the slice is not treated long enough, the white matter may appear mottled after staining. Spotting of white matter may be produced by cross-contamination of solutions or by the scraping off of portions of the protective film due to rough handling of slices. For protection of the film, slices should never be washed directly under a water tap; they must be carefully slipped into each solution. Teflon spatulas facilitate the gentle handling of slices.

After remaining in the hot copper sulfate-phenol solution for 6 minutes (a procedure best carried out under a hood) the slice is washed in cold tap water for 1 minute and then in running water for 6 minutes (conveniently done in a 5-gallon Nalgene tank). It is then placed in 1.5 liters of freshly prepared 1.5% solution of potassium ferrocyanide in a large, shallow Pyrex dish until the proper red-brown color develops, usually within 30 to 60 seconds. The section is washed again for 6 minutes in running water, and then stored in 10% formalin. Some fading can be expected after a few months.

Careful choice of specimens is necessary to produce consistently satisfactory results. Brains from patients over 60 years of age frequently stain irregularly. Brains from the elderly also tend to fragment during slicing.

The coronal sections appearing in this atlas were taken from the brain of a 22-year-old white woman who had been in good health until 6 months prior to her death when a hemangio-endothelioma was removed from the retro-peritoneal space. The patient never had any symptoms suggestive of central nervous system disease. She died with extensive involvement of both lungs by the neoplasm.

The horizontal sections were made from the brain of a 58-year-old white man who was found to have adenocarcinoma of the right kidney 1 year prior to death. The patient died with extensive metastases to the pelvic bones and lungs. He never had any symptoms of central nervous system involvement.

The sagittal sections were cut from the brain of a 35-year-old Negro woman who had chronic glomerulonephritis, and died in uremia. She had no known central nervous system disease.

Photographic Method

A 5 × 7 view camera with a 300-mm Schneider Symmar 5.6 lens was used to photograph all of the sections. To increase contrast, a Kodak #58 green filter was employed. So that the sections would appear on a white background they were illuminated from behind by an x-ray view box containing two 15-watt daylight fluorescent lamps. The light background improved the appearance of the pictures and also afforded better demonstration of structures such as sulci, ventricles, and meninges. Front lighting was produced by two 500-watt 3200 K floodlamps with reflectors. Exposure was for 1 second at F16. Tri-X orthochromatic film was developed in Kodak Polydol for 9 minutes at 68° F. A 5 × 7 condenser enlarger was used to print the negatives on Polycontrast F paper.

Terminology and Labeling

Although Latin has the advantage of universal usage, most students in this country prefer English terms. For this reason two sets of terminology have been used throughout this atlas. Each structure is identified by its common English name as well as a Latin equivalent. Because there is no single authoritative source containing all terms in either English or Latin our choice of necessity has been arbitrary at times. Most of the Latin terms are those recommended by the International Anatomical Nomenclature Committee and approved at the Sixth, Seventh, and Eighth International Congresses of Anatomists held at Paris in 1955, at New York in 1960, and at Wiesbaden in 1965. Terms not found in the Nomina Anatomica were taken from Singer and Yakovlev's atlas, *The Human Brain in Sagittal Section*, and Riley's *Atlas of the Basal Ganglia, Brain Stem and Spinal Cord*. Most of the English terms are those used in Crosby, Humphrey and Lauer's *Correlative Anatomy of the Nervous System*, and Truex and Carpenter's edition of Strong and Elwyn's *Human Neuroanatomy*.

The labeling system was devised after much deliberation. Virtually all methods were considered. Numbers, rather than abbreviations or entire terms, were chosen for many reasons. Numbers, arranged serially clockwise, allow the reader to locate immediately a structure without having to search through the entire section in an attempt to find a specific symbol or term. Numbers also make self-testing convenient for the student. For this reason, any sort of numbering code has purposely been avoided.

Leaders were used so that numbers could be arranged orderly to facilitate rapid identification of structures. It was found that the over-all appearance of the sections was better when leaders were employed than when the labels were placed directly on the specimens. Leaders also permit greater precision, particularly in pointing out smaller areas. Because of the number of structures identified it was impossible to label all on every section. Structures that appear repeatedly have been labeled on alternate plates or, in some instances, even less frequently. Labeling was done in pencil on a tracing paper overlay and then transferred to an acetate overlay using cutout lines and numerals supplied by the publisher.

ACKNOWLEDGMENTS

This atlas could not have been produced without the assistance of many. We are particularly grateful for the assistance received from colleagues at the University of Virginia School of Medicine—Mr. Richard A. Mason and Miss Anne Russell, of the Section of Medical Photography, for the fine photographs; Mr. William E. Fairweather, Mr. Joseph C. Eddins and Miss Jan Franks, of the Section of Medical Art, for the preparation of the acetate overlays; Dr. W. Gayle Crutchfield, Professor of Neurological Surgery, and Dr. Jan Langman, Professor of Anatomy, for help and encouragement; and Professor Arthur Stocker for advice on the Latin terms. The specimens were obtained through the kindness of Dr. David E. Smith, Professor of Pathology, and Dr. Martin G. Netsky, Professor of Pathology, with the aid of Mr. Lester Perry. We are indebted to Dr. Kenneth R. Crispell, Dean of the School of Medicine, and Dr. Warren G. Stamp, Professor of Orthopedics, through whose generosity laboratory space was made available. We also wish to express our appreciation to Miss Jeanne Weaver and Mrs. Lucille Staiger for the many hours spent in preparing the index and typing the manuscript. Finally we extend thanks to Mr. Martin C. Dallago and Mr. Thomas Colaiezzi, of Lea & Febiger, for their cooperation and helpfulness during the preparation and publication of this atlas.

MELVILLE ROBERTS
JOSEPH HANAWAY
Charlottesville, Virginia

REFERENCES

Andrianov, C. C., and Mering, T. A., 1959: Atlas of the Brain of the Dog. Moscow, Moscow State Publishing House for Medical Literature.

Angevine, J. B., Mancall, E. L., and Yakovlev, P. I., 1961: The Human Cerebellum. Boston, Little, Brown & Company.

Ariens Kappers, C. U., Huber, G. C., and Crosby, E. C., 1936: The Comparative Anatomy of the Nervous System of Vertebrates, Including Man. New York, Macmillan Co.

Berman, A. L., 1968: The Brain Stem of the Cat. Madison, University of Wisconsin Press.

Clark, W. E. LeGros, 1938: The Hypothalamus. London, Oliver and Boyd, Ltd.

Crosby, E. C., Humphrey, T., and Lauer, E. W., 1962: Correlative Anatomy of the Nervous System. New York, Macmillan Co.

International Anatomical Nomenclature Committee of the Fifth International Congress of Anatomists, 1968: Nomina Anatomica. Amsterdam, Excerpta Medica Foundation.

Jasper, H. H., and Ajmone-Marson, C., 1957: A Stereotaxic Atlas of the Diencephalon of the Cat. Ottawa, Canada, National Research Council.

Jelgersma, G., 1931: Atlas Anatomicum Cerebri Humani. Amsterdam, Schettema and Holkema.

Kampmeier, O. F., and Hospodar, E. W., 1951: Mounting of stained serial slices of the brain as wet specimens in transparent plastic. Anat. Rec. 110: 1–15.

Kuhlenbeck, H., 1954: The Human Diencephalon. Basel and New York, S. Karger.

Lim, R. K. S., Liu C., and Moffitt, R. L., 1960: A Stereotaxic Atlas of the Dog Brain. Springfield, Ill., Charles C Thomas.

Ludwig, E., and Klingler, J., 1956: Atlas Cerebri Humani. Basel and New York, S. Karger.

Mettler, F. A., 1951: Neuroanatomy. St. Louis, C. V. Mosby Co.

Miller, R. A., and Burack, E., 1968: Atlas of the Central Nervous System in Man. Baltimore, Williams & Wilkins Co.

Monnier, M., 1949: A Short Atlas of the Brain Stem of the Cat and Rhesus Monkey for Experimental Research. Vienna, Springer-Verlag.

Mulligan, J. H., 1931: A method of staining the brain for macroscopic study. J. Anat. 65: 468–472.

Olszewski, J., 1952: The Thalamus of the Macacca Mulatta. An Atlas for Use with Stereotaxic Instruments. New York, S. Karger.

Olszewski, J., and Baxter, D., 1954: Cytoarchitecture of the Human Brain Stem. Philadelphia, J. B. Lippincott Co.

Pernkopf, E., 1963: Atlas of Topographical and Applied Human Anatomy. Edited by H. Ferner. Philadelphia, W. B. Saunders Co.

Roberts, M., and Hanaway, J., 1969: Preparation of brain slices for macroscopic study by the copper sulfate-phenol-ferrocyanide technique. Stain Technol., 44:143–146.

Riley, H. A., 1943: Atlas of the Basal Ganglia, Brain Stem and Spinal Cord. Baltimore, Williams & Wilkins Co.

Schaltenbrand, G., and Bailey, P., 1952: Introduction to Stereotaxis with an Atlas of the Human Brain. Stuttgart, Georg Thieme Verlag.

Shade, J. P., and Ford, D., 1966: Atlas of the Human Brain. New York, Elsevier Publishing Co.

Singer, M., 1962: The Brain of the Dog in Section. Philadelphia, W. B. Saunders Co.

Singer, M., and Yakovlev, P. I., 1954: The Human Brain in Sagittal Section. Springfield, Ill., Charles C Thomas.

Sobotta, J., 1963: Atlas of Human Anatomy. Edited by F. H. J. Figge. New York, Hafner Publishing Co.

Snider, R. S., and Lee J. C., 1961: A Stereotaxic Atlas of the Monkey Brain. Chicago, University of Chicago Press.

Snider, R. S., and Niemer, W. T., 1961: A Stereotaxic Atlas of the Cat Brain. Chicago, University of Chicago Press.

Stelmesiak, M., 1956: Anatomical Atlas of the Human Brain and Spinal Cord. Warsaw, Polish State Medical Publishers.

Truex, R. C., and Carpenter, M. B., 1964: Strong and Elwyn's Human Neuroanatomy. Baltimore, Williams & Wilkins Co.

Villeger, E., Ludwig, E., and Rasmussen, A. T., 1951: Atlas of Cross Section Anatomy of the Brain. New York, McGraw-Hill Book Co.

CORONAL SECTIONS

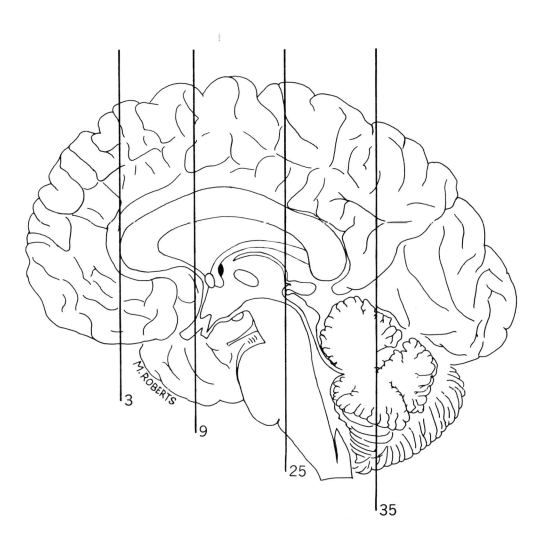

M. ROBERTS

3

9

25

35

Anterior Surface of Coronal Section through Rostal Wall of Lateral Ventricle X1.5

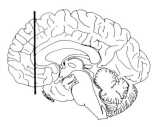

1.	Longitudinal cerebral fissure	Fissura longitudinalis cerebri
2.	Superior frontal gyrus	Gyrus frontalis superior
3.	Superior frontal sulcus	Sulcus frontalis superior
4.	Cingulate artery	Arteria cinguli
5.	Cingulum	Cingulum
6.	Sulcus of corpus callosum	Sulcus corporis callosi
7.	Radiations of corpus callosum	Radiatio corporis callosi
8.	Intracerebral anastomatic veins	Venae anastomaticae intracerebres
9.	Inferior occipitofrontal fasciculus	Fasciculus occipitofrontalis inferior
10.	Orbital gyri	Gyri orbitales
11.	Olfactory sulcus	Sulcus olfactorius
12.	Longitudinal cerebral fissure	Fissura longitudinalis cerebri
13.	Straight gyrus	Gyrus rectus
14.	Medial orbital gyrus	Gyrus orbitalis medialis
15.	Anterior cerebral artery	Arteria cerebri anterior
16.	Genu of corpus callosum	Genu corporis callosi
17.	Superior occipitofrontal fasciculus	Fasciculus occipitofrontalis superior
18.	Inferior frontal gyrus	Gyrus frontalis inferior
19.	Inferior frontal sulcus	Sulcus frontalis inferior
20.	Middle frontal gyrus	Gyrus frontalis medius
21.	Pericallosal artery	Arteria pericallosa
22.	Cingulate gyrus	Gyrus cinguli
23.	Cingulate sulcus	Sulcus cinguli
24.	Superior frontal gyrus	Gyrus frontalis superior

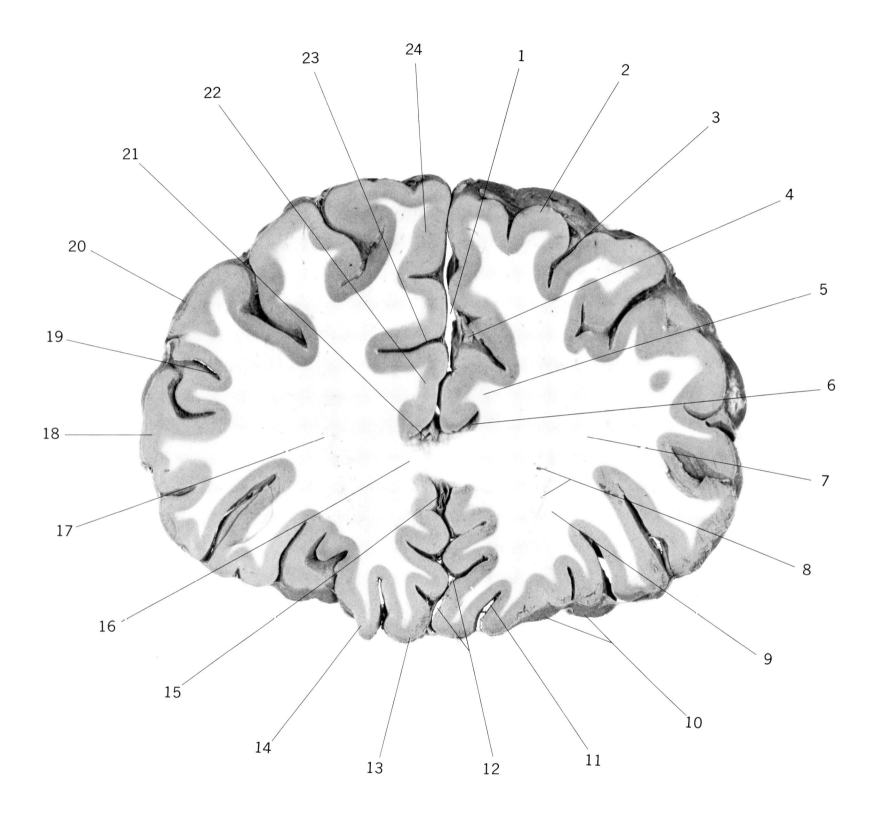

Posterior Surface of Coronal Section through Anterior Limit of Putamen X1.5

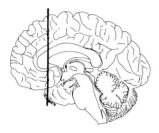

1. Longitudinal cerebral fissure — Fissura longitudinalis cerebri
2. Superior frontal gyrus — Gyrus frontalis superior
3. Pericallosal artery — Arteria pericallosa
4. Sulcus of corpus callosum — Sulcus corporis callosi
5. Body of corpus callosum — Truncus corporis callosi
6. Lamina of septum pellucidum — Lamina septi pellucidi
7. Anterior horn of lateral ventricle — Cornu anterius ventriculi lateralis
8. Circular sulcus of insula — Sulcus circularis insulae
9. Inferior frontal gyrus — Gyrus frontalis inferior
10. Lateral cerebral fissure — Fissura lateralis cerebri
11. Head of caudate nucleus — Caput nuclei caudati
12. Cavum of septum pellucidum — Cavum septi pellucidi
13. Rostrum of corpus callosum — Rostrum corporis callosi
14. Olfactory sulcus — Sulcus olfactorius
15. Straight gyrus — Gyrus rectus
16. Longitudinal cerebral fissure — Fissura longitudinalis cerebri
17. Anterior cerebral artery — Arteria cerebri anterior
18. Olfactory tract — Tractus olfactorius
19. Orbital gyri — Gyri orbitales
20. Middle temporal gyrus — Gyrus temporalis medius
21. Superior temporal gyrus — Gyrus temporalis superior
22. Putamen — Putamen
23. Short gyri of insula — Gyri breves insulae
24. Anterior limb of internal capsule — Crus anterius capsulae internae
25. Superior longitudinal fasciculus — Fasciculus longitudinalis superior
26. Superior occipitofrontal fasciculus — Fasciculus occipitofrontalis superior
27. Middle frontal gyrus — Gyrus frontalis medius
28. Superior frontal sulcus — Sulcus frontalis superior
29. Cingulum — Cingulum
30. Cingulate sulcus — Sulcus cinguli
31. Cingulate gyrus — Gyrus cinguli

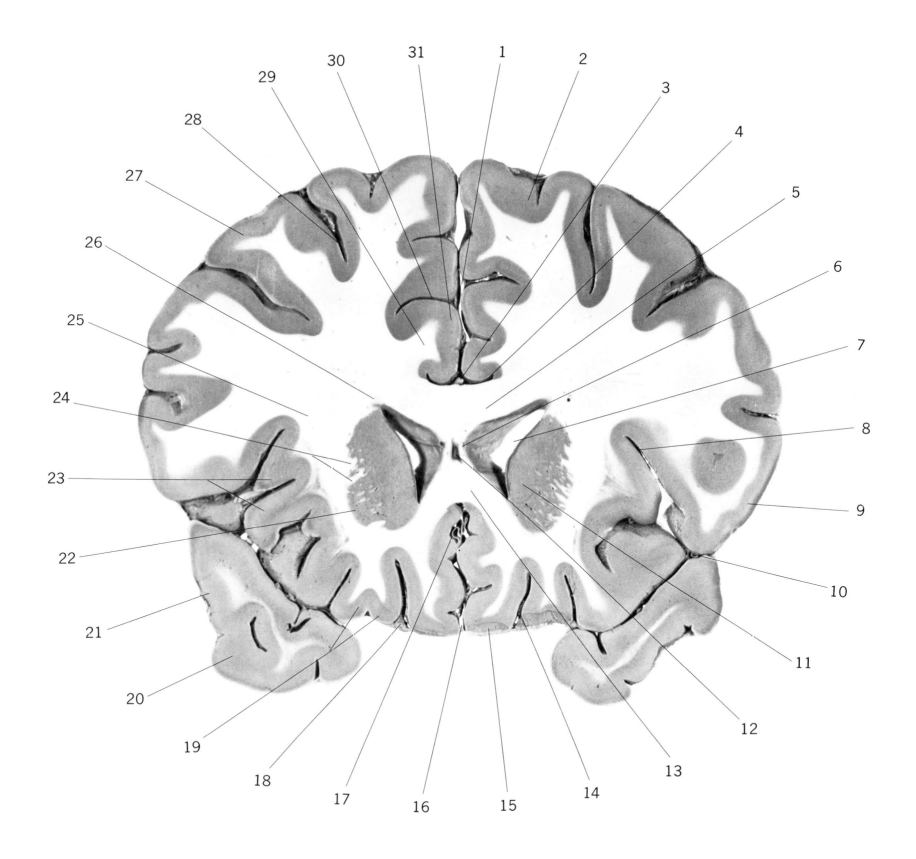

Anterior Surface of Coronal Section through Head of Caudate Nucleus and Putamen X1.5

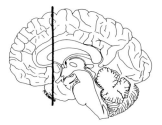

1.	Sulcus of corpus callosum	Sulcus corporis callosi
2.	Superior frontal sulcus	Sulcus frontalis superior
3.	Anterior horn of lateral ventricle	Cornu anterius ventriculi lateralis
4.	Head of caudate nucleus	Caput nuclei caudati
5.	Inferior frontal sulcus	Sulcus frontalis inferior
6.	Corona radiata	Corona radiata
7.	Transcapsular caudatolenticular gray striae	Striae griseae caudatolenticulares transcapsulares
8.	External capsule	Capsula externa
9.	Claustrum	Claustrum
10.	Putamen	Putamen
11.	Middle temporal gyrus	Gyrus temporalis medius
12.	Cingulate gyrus	Gyrus cinguli
13.	Inferior temporal sulcus	Sulcus temporalis inferior
14.	Straight gyrus	Gyrus rectus
15.	Anterior cerebral artery	Arteria cerebri anterior
16.	Cingulum	Cingulum
17.	Inferior temporal gyrus	Gyrus temporalis inferior
18.	Colliculus of caudate nucleus	Colliculus nuclei caudati
19.	Middle cerebral artery	Arteria cerebri media
20.	Extreme capsule	Capsula extrema
21.	Superior temporal sulcus	Sulcus temporalis superior
22.	Superior temporal gyrus	Gyrus temporalis superior
23.	Anterior limb of internal capsule	Crus anterius capsulae internae
24.	Inferior frontal gyrus	Gyrus frontalis inferior
25.	Septum pellucidum	Septum pellucidum
26.	Middle frontal gyrus	Gyrus frontalis medius
27.	Cingulum	Cingulum
28.	Cingulate gyrus	Gyrus cinguli
29.	Superior frontal gyrus	Gyrus frontalis superior
30.	Cingulate artery	Arteria cinguli

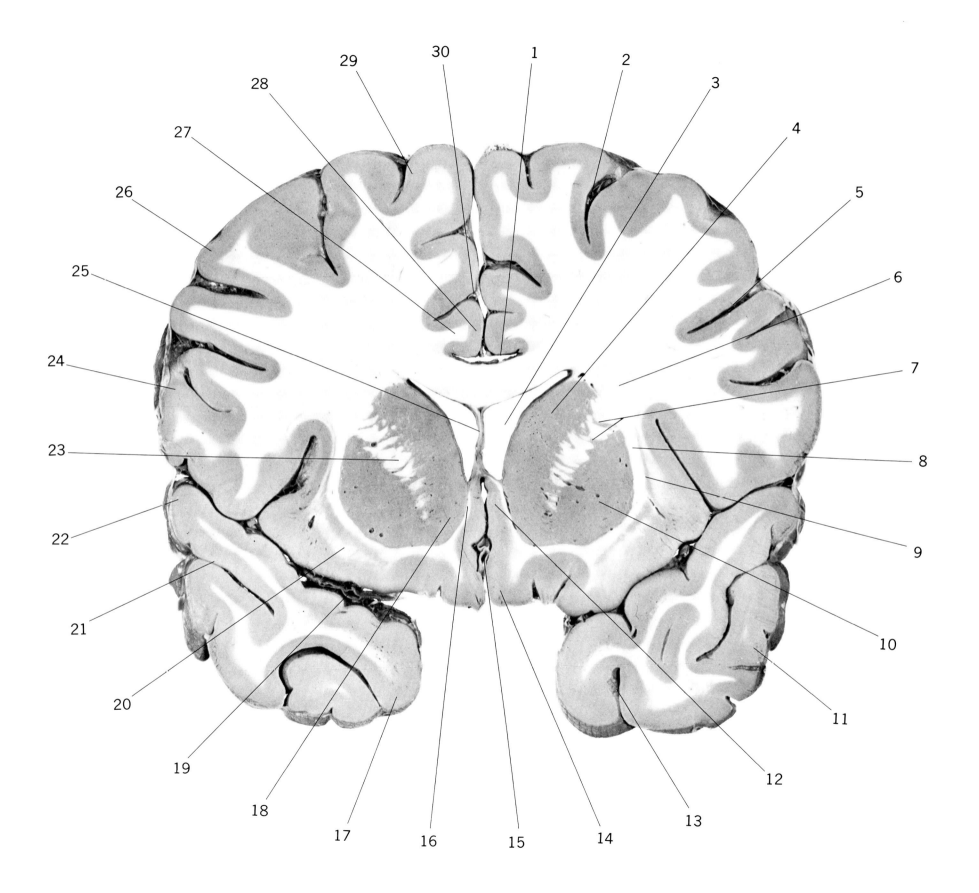

Posterior Surface of Coronal Section through Anterior Limit of Amygdala X1.5

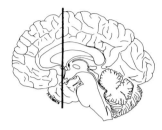

1.	Pericallosal artery	Arteria pericallosa
2.	Body of corpus callosum	Truncus corporis callosi
3.	Stylus of septum pellucidum	Stylus septi pellucidi
4.	Head of caudate nucleus	Caput nuclei caudati
5.	Anterior limb of internal capsule	Crus anterius capsulae internae
6.	Globus pallidus II	Globus pallidus II
7.	Extreme capsule	Capsula extrema
8.	Insula	Insula
9.	Putamen	Putamen·
10.	Lateral cerebral fissure	Fissura lateralis cerebri
11.	Uncinate fasciculus	Fasciculus uncinatus
12.	Lenticulostriate branches of middle cerebral artery	Rami lenticulostriati arteriae cerebralis mediae
13.	Olfactory part of anterior commissure	Pars olfactoria commissurae anterioris
14.	Middle cerebral artery	Arteria cerebri media
15.	Anterior cerebral artery	Arteria cerebri anterior
16.	Internal carotid artery	Arteria carotis interna
17.	Optic chiasm	Chiasma opticum
18.	Olfactory area	Area olfactoria
19.	Anterior perforated substance	Substantia perforata anterior
20.	Amygdala	Corpus amygdaloideum
21.	Anterior commissure	Commissura anterior
22.	Orbitofrontal fibers	Fibrae orbitofrontalis
23.	Inferior occipitofrontal fasciculus	Fasciculus occipitofrontalis inferior
24.	Middle cerebral artery	Arteria cerebri media
25.	Claustrum	Claustrum
26.	External medullary lamina of globus pallidus	Lamina medullaris externa pallidi
27.	External capsule	Capsula externa
28.	Superior longitudinal fasciculus	Fasciculus longitudinalis superior
29.	Corona radiata	Corona radiata
30.	Superior occipitofrontal fasciculus	Fasciculus occipitofrontalis superior
31.	Anterior horn of lateral ventricle	Cornu anterius ventriculi lateralis
32.	Septum pellucidum	Septum pellucidum
33.	Longitudinal cerebral fissure	Fissura longitudinalis cerebri

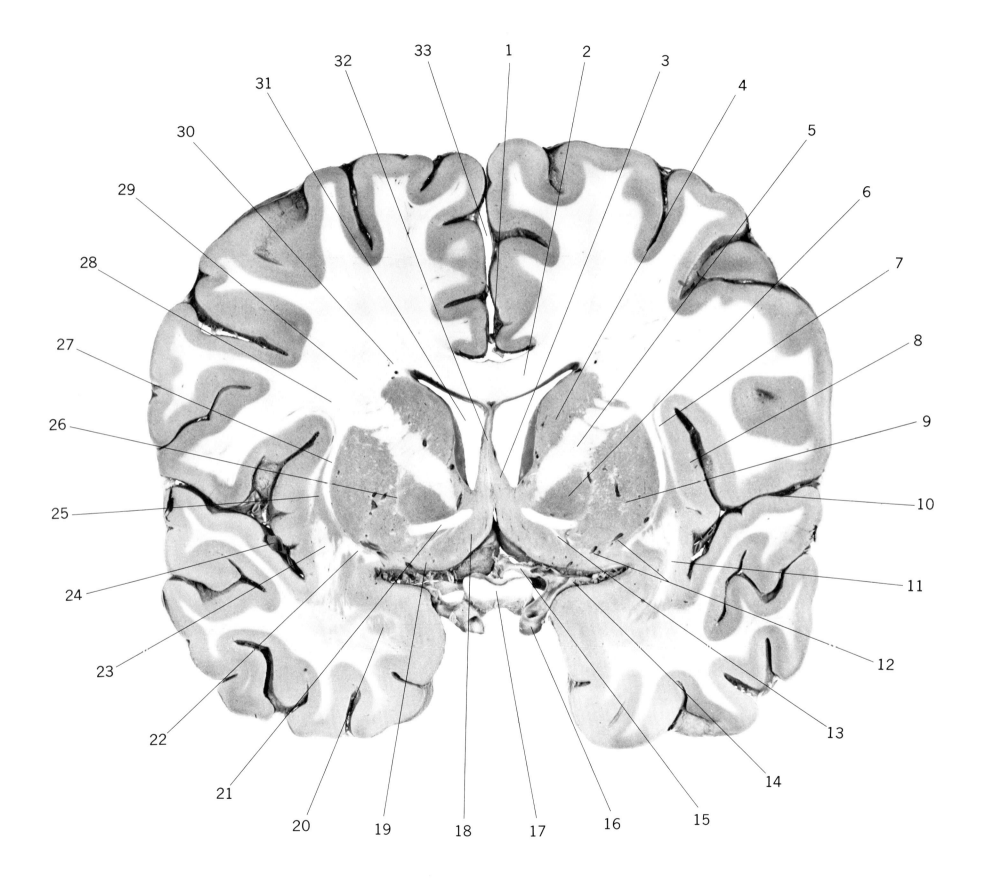

Posterior Surface of Coronal Sections through Tuber Cinereum X1.5

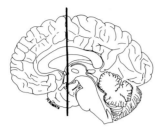

1.	Superior frontal gyrus	Gyrus frontalis superior
2.	Sulcus of corpus callosum	Sulcus corporis callosi
3.	Head of caudate nucleus	Caput nuclei caudati
4.	Middle frontal gyrus	Gyrus frontalis medius
5.	Corona radiata	Corona radiata
6.	External capsule	Capsula externa
7.	Inferior frontal gyrus	Gyrus frontalis inferior
8.	Extreme capsule	Capsula extrema
9.	Globus pallidus I and II	Globus pallidus I et II
10.	Anterior commissure	Commissura anterior
11.	Anterior commissure	Commissura anterior
12.	Amygdala	Corpus amygdaloideum
13.	Dorsal supraoptic commissure	Commissura supraoptica dorsalis
14.	Optic tract	Tractus opticus
15.	Infundibulum	Infundibulum
16.	Tuber cinereum	Tuber cinereum
17.	Ventral supraoptic commissure	Commissura supraoptica ventralis
18.	Column of fornix	Columna fornicis
19.	Internal medullary lamina of globus pallidus	Lamina medullaris interna pallidi
20.	Lenticulostriate branches of middle cerebral artery	Rami lenticulostriati arteriae cerebralis mediae
21.	External medullary lamina of globus pallidus	Lamina medullaris externa pallidi
22.	Lateral cerebral fissure	Fissura lateralis cerebri
23.	Putamen	Putamen
24.	Claustrum	Claustrum
25.	Anterior limb of internal capsule	Crus anterius capsulae internae
26.	Inferior frontal sulcus	Sulcus frontalis inferior
27.	Superior occipitofrontal fasciculus	Fasciculus occipitofrontalis superior
28.	Superior frontal sulcus	Sulcus frontalis superior
29.	Body of corpus callosum	Truncus corporis callosi
30.	Cingulate sulcus	Sulcus cinguli

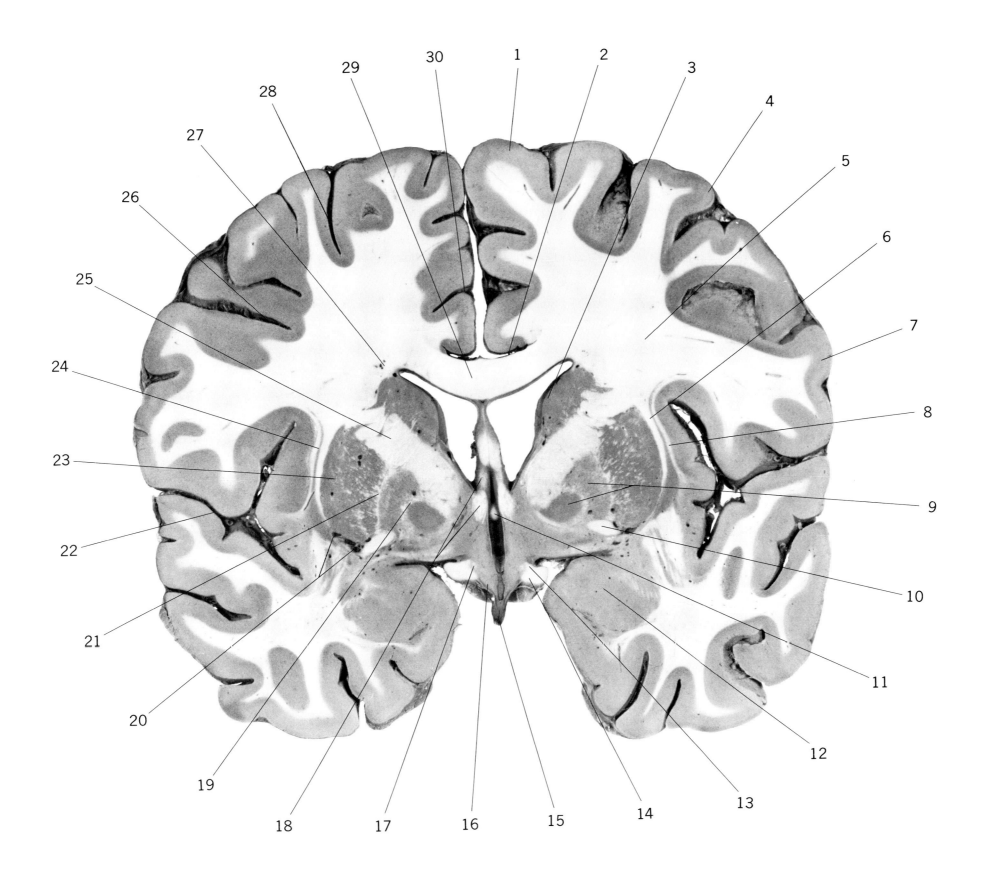

Anterior Surface of Coronal Section through Interventricular Foramen X1.5

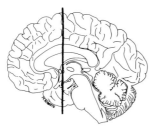

1.	Cingulate artery	Arteria cinguli
2.	Cingulate gyrus	Gyrus cinguli
3.	Cingulum	Cingulum
4.	Body of corpus callosum	Truncus corporis callosi
5.	Body of lateral ventricle	Corpus ventriculi lateralis
6.	Head of caudate nucleus	Caput nuclei caudati
7.	Body of fornix	Corpus fornicis
8.	Claustrum	Claustrum
9.	Globus pallidus II	Globus pallidus II
10.	Circular sulcus of insula	Sulcus circularis insulae
11.	Anterior commissure	Commissura anterior
12.	Globus pallidus I	Globus pallidus I
13.	Column of fornix	Columna fornicis
14.	Dorsal supraoptic commissure	Commissura supraoptica dorsalis
15.	Third ventricle	Ventriculus tertius
16.	Ventral supraoptic commissure	Commissura supraoptica ventralis
17.	Optic tract	Tractus opticus
18.	Olfactory fasciculus	Fasciculus olfactorius
19.	Interventricular foramen	Foramen interventriculare
20.	Internal medullary lamina of globus pallidus	Lamina medullaris interna pallidi
21.	External medullary lamina of globus pallidus	Lamina medullaris externa pallidi
22.	Putamen	Putamen
23.	Insula	Insula
24.	Extreme capsule	Capsula extrema
25.	External capsule	Capsula externa
26.	Genu of internal capsule	Genu capsulae internae
27.	Middle frontal gyrus	Gyrus frontalis medius
28.	Choroid plexus of lateral ventricle	Plexus choroideus ventriculi lateralis
29.	Septum pellucidum	Septum pellucidum
30.	Longitudinal cerebral fissure	Fissura longitudinalis cerebri

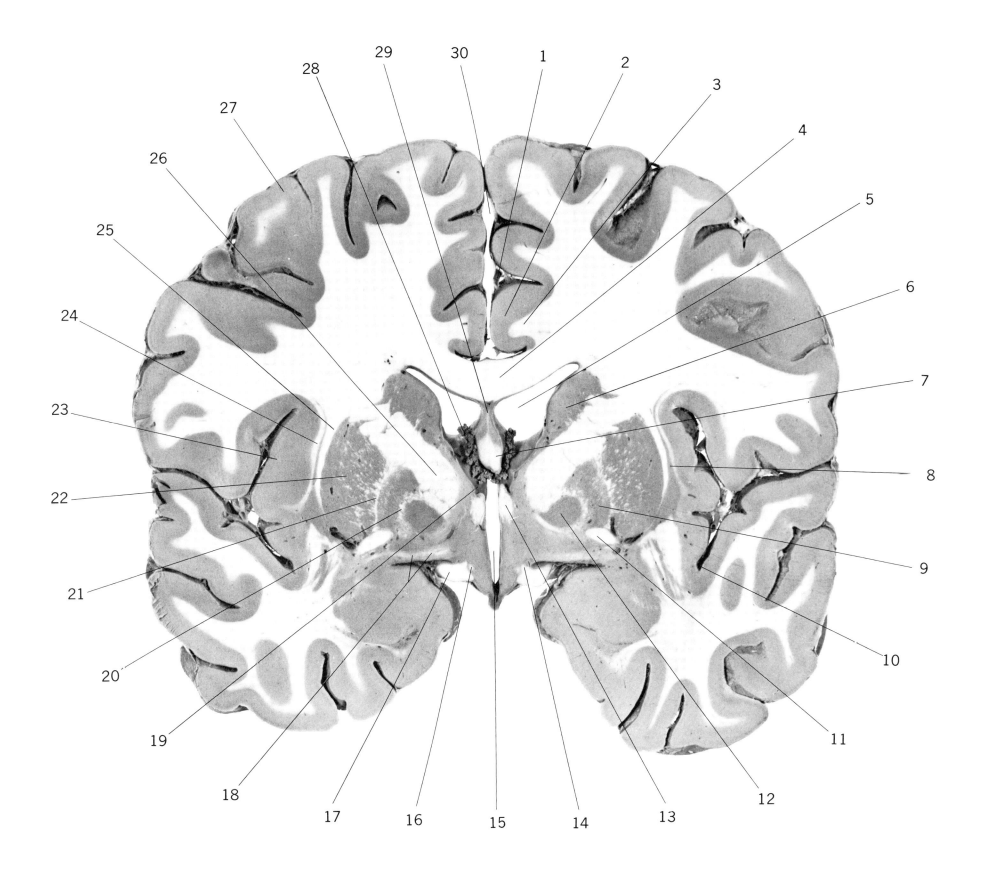

Anterior Surface of Coronal Section through Anterodorsal Nucleus of Thalamus X1.5

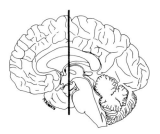

1.	Body of corpus callosum	Truncus corporis callosi
2.	Superior frontal gyrus	Gyrus frontalis superior
3.	Superior frontal sulcus	Sulcus frontalis superior
4.	Stria medullaris of thalamus	Stria medullaris thalami
5.	Middle frontal gyrus	Gyrus frontalis medius
6.	Tail of caudate nucleus	Cauda nuclei caudati
7.	Third ventricle	Ventriculus tertius
8.	Interthalamic adhesion	Adhesio interthalamica
9.	External medullary lamina of globus pallidus	Lamina medullaris externa pallidi
10.	Internal medullary lamina of globus pallidus	Lamina medullaris interna pallidi
11.	Incomplete medullary lamina of globus pallidus	Lamina medullaris incompleta pallidi
12.	Ansa lenticularis	Ansa lenticularis
13.	Optic tract	Tractus opticus
14.	Alveus of hippocampus	Alveus hippocampi
15.	Collateral sulcus	Sulcus collateralis
16.	Parahippocampal gyrus	Gyrus parahippocampalis
17.	Uncus	Uncus
18.	Third ventricle	Ventriculus tertius
19.	Column of fornix	Columna fornicis
20.	Anterior ventral nucleus of thalamus	Nucleus ventralis anterior thalami
21.	Lateral occipitotemporal gyrus	Gyrus occipitotemporalis lateralis
22.	Hippocampus	Hippocampus
23.	Inferior temporal gyrus	Gyrus temporalis inferior
24.	Amygdala	Corpus amygdaloideum
25.	Middle temporal gyrus	Gyrus temporalis medius
26.	Superior temporal sulcus	Sulcus temporalis superior
27.	Superior temporal gyrus	Gyrus temporalis superior
28.	Inferior frontal gyrus	Gyrus frontalis inferior
29.	Putamen	Putamen
30.	Claustrum	Claustrum
31.	Globus pallidus I and II	Globus pallidus I et II
32.	Posterior limb of internal capsule	Crus posterius capsulae internae
33.	Internal medullary lamina of thalamus	Lamina medullaris interna thalami
34.	Anterodorsal nucleus of thalamus	Nucleus anterodorsalis thalami
35.	Body of fornix	Corpus fornicis

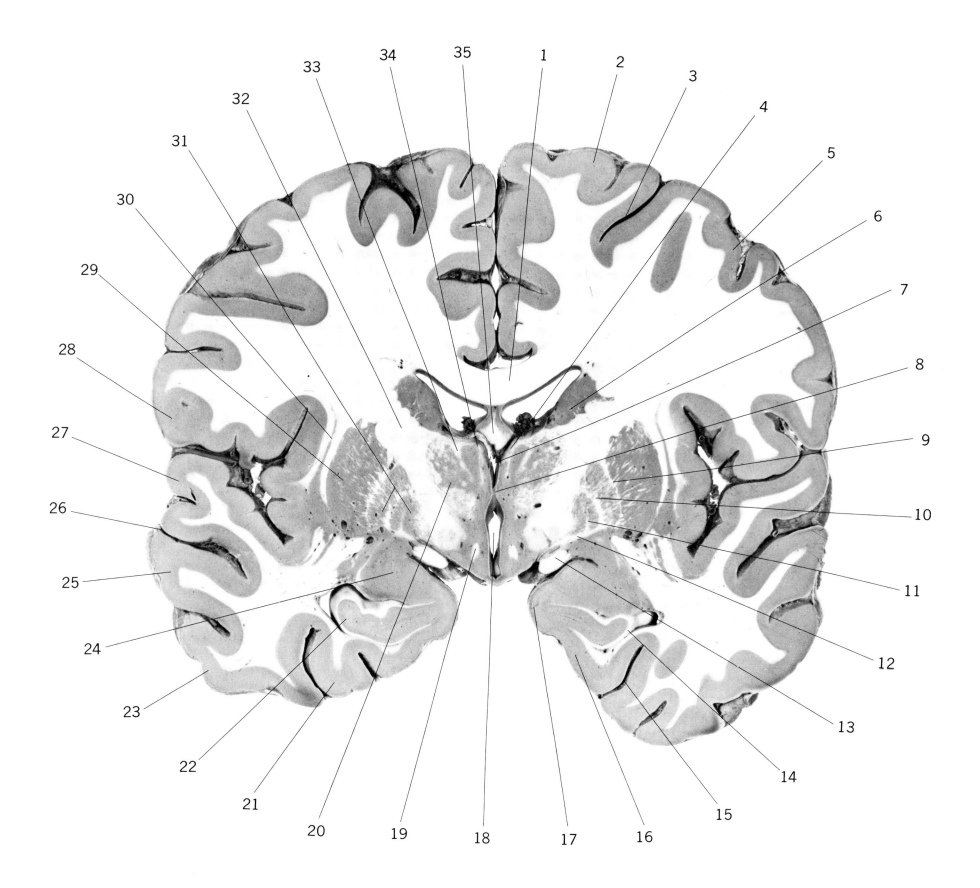

15

Posterior Surface of Coronal Section through
Mamillothalamic Fasciculus X1.5

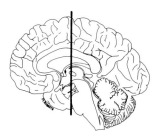

	English	Latin
1.	Cingulate gyrus	Gyrus cinguli
2.	Third ventricle	Ventriculus tertius
3.	Anteroventral nucleus of thalamus	Nucleus anteroventralis thalami
4.	Superior occipitofrontal fasciculus	Fasciculus occipitofrontalis superior
5.	Tail of caudate nucleus	Cauda nuclei caudati
6.	Transcapsular caudatolenticular gray striae	Striae griseae caudatolenticulares transcapsulares
7.	Precentral gyrus	Gyrus precentralis
8.	Central sulcus	Sulcus centralis
9.	Postcentral gyrus	Gyrus postcentralis
10.	Superior temporal gyrus	Gyrus temporalis superior
11.	Middle cerebral artery	Arteria cerebri media
12.	Superior temporal sulcus	Sulcus temporalis superior
13.	Dorsal medial nucleus of thalamus	Nucleus medialis dorsalis thalami
14.	Inferior horn of lateral ventricle	Cornu inferius ventriculi lateralis
15.	Optic tract	Tractus opticus
16.	Lateral occipitotemporal gyrus	Gyrus occipitotemporalis lateralis
17.	Parahippocampal gyrus	Gyrus parahippocampalis
18.	Tegmental area H_2	Area tegmentalis H_2
19.	Mamillary body	Corpus mamillare
20.	Third ventricle	Ventriculus tertius
21.	Principle mamillothalamic fasciculus	Fasciculus mamillaris princeps
22.	Substantia nigra	Substantia nigra
23.	Collateral sulcus	Sulcus collateralis
24.	Dentate gyrus	Gyrus dentatus
25.	Inferior temporal gyrus	Gyrus temporalis inferior
26.	Subthalamic nucleus	Nucleus subthalamicus
27.	Zona incerta	Zona incerta
28.	Globus pallidus I and II	Globus pallidus I et II
29.	Tegmental area H_1	Area tegmentalis H_1
30.	Putamen	Putamen
31.	External medullary lamina of thalamus	Lamina medullaris externa thalami
32.	Posterior limb of internal capsule	Crus posterius capsulae internae
33.	Mamillothalamic fasciculus	Fasciculus mamillothalamicus
34.	Posterior lateral nucleus of thalamus	Nucleus lateralis posterior thalami
35.	Body of lateral ventricle	Corpus ventriculi lateralis
36.	Choroid plexus of lateral ventricle	Plexus choroideus ventriculi lateralis
37.	Body of corpus callosum	Truncus corporis callosi
38.	Superior frontal gyrus	Gyrus frontalis superior

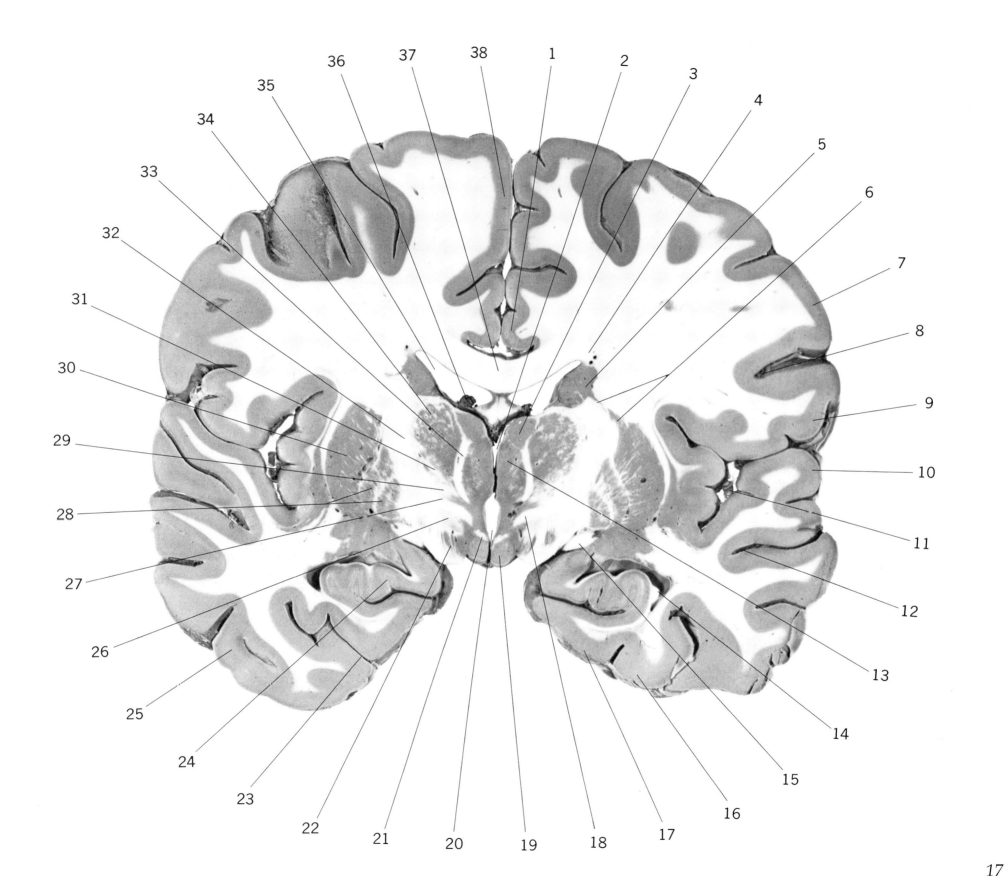

Anterior Surface of Coronal Section through Mamillary Bodies X1.5

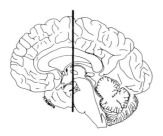

1. Cingulate artery   Arteria cinguli
2. Body of fornix   Corpus fornicis
3. Interthalamic adhesion   Adhesio interthalamica
4. Anteroventral nucleus of thalamus   Nucleus anteroventralis thalami
5. Stria terminalis and thalamostriate vein   Stria terminalis et vena thalamostriata
6. Tail of caudate nucleus   Cauda nuclei caudati
7. Lateral ventral nucleus of thalamus   Nucleus ventralis lateralis thalami
8. Mamillothalamic fasciculus   Fasciculus mamillothalamicus
9. Claustrum   Claustrum
10. External capsule   Capsula externa
11. Lenticulostriate branches of middle cerebral artery   Rami lenticulostriati arteriae cerebralis mediae
12. Globus pallidus II   Globus pallidus II
13. Globus pallidus I   Globus pallidus I
14. Zona incerta   Zona incerta
15. Subthalamic nucleus   Nucleus subthalamicus
16. Substantia nigra   Substantia nigra
17. Cerebral peduncle   Pedunculus cerebri
18. Posterior cerebral artery   Arteria cerebri posterior
19. Principle mamillary fasciculus   Fasciculus mamillaris princeps
20. Basilar artery   Arteria basilaris
21. Pons   Pons
22. Interpeduncular fossa   Fossa interpeduncularis
23. Mamillary body   Corpus mamillare
24. Third ventricle   Ventriculus tertius
25. Hippocampal sulcus   Sulcus hippocampi
26. Hippocampus   Hippocampus
27. Alveus of hippocampus   Alveus hippocampi
28. Inferior horn of lateral ventricle   Cornu inferius ventriculi lateralis
29. Amygdala   Corpus amygdaloideum
30. Optic tract   Tractus opticus
31. Internal medullary lamina of globus pallidus   Lamina medullaris interna pallidi
32. External medullary lamina of globus pallidus   Lamina medullaris externa pallidi
33. Extreme capsule   Capsula extrema
34. Putamen   Putamen
35. Posterior limb of internal capsule   Crus posterius capsulae internae
36. Rostral peduncle of thalamus   Pedunculus rostralis thalami
37. Tegmental area H_2 Area tegmentalis H_2
38. Velum interpositum   Velum interpositum

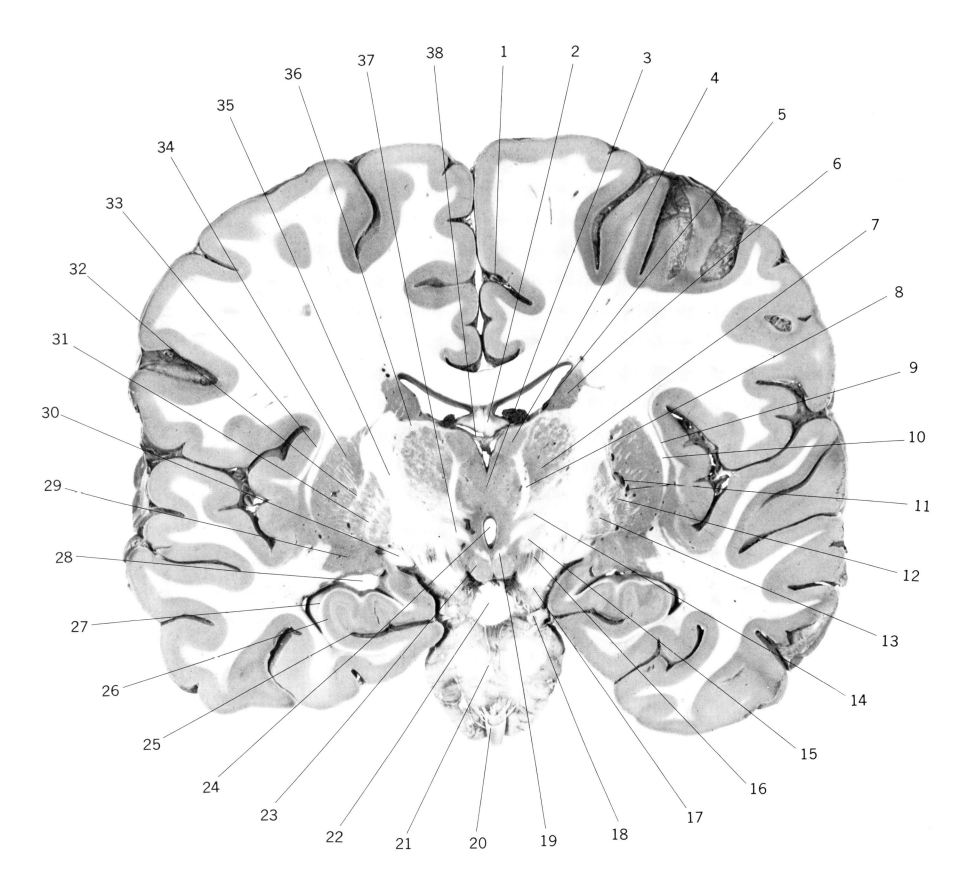

Anterior Surface of Coronal Section through Subthalamic Nucleus X1.5

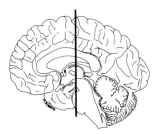

1.	Cingulate gyrus	Gyrus cinguli
2.	Body of corpus callosum	Truncus corporis callosi
3.	Velum interpositum and tela choroidea	Velum interpositum et tela choroidea
4.	Choroid plexus of lateral ventricle	Plexus choroideus ventriculi lateralis
5.	Tail of caudate nucleus	Cauda nuclei caudati
6.	Anteroventral nucleus of thalamus	Nucleus anteroventralis thalami
7.	Postcentral gyrus	Gyrus postcentralis
8.	Putamen	Putamen
9.	Posterior limb of internal capsule	Crus posterius capsulae internae
10.	Posterolateral ventral nucleus of thalamus	Nucleus ventralis posterolateralis thalami
11.	Hypothalamus	Hypothalamus
12.	Amygdala	Corpus amygdaloideum
13.	Tail of caudate nucleus	Cauda nuclei caudati
14.	Optic tract	Tractus opticus
15.	Hippocampus	Hippocampus
16.	Hippocampal sulcus	Sulcus hippocampi
17.	Substantia nigra	Substantia nigra
18.	Third ventricle	Ventriculus tertius
19.	Corticospinal tract	Tractus corticospinalis
20.	Ventral decussation of pons	Decussatio ventralis pontis
21.	Superficial transverse fibers of pons	Fibrae transversae superficiales pontis
22.	Interpeduncular fossa	Fossa interpeduncularis
23.	Middle cerebellar peduncle	Pedunculus cerebellaris medius
24.	Parahippocampal gyrus	Gyrus parahippocampalis
25.	Lateral occipitotemporal gyrus	Gyrus occipitotemporalis lateralis
26.	Cerebral peduncle	Pedunculus cerebri
27.	Choroid plexus of inferior horn of lateral ventricle	Plexus choroideus ventriculi lateralis cornu inferius
28.	Subthalamic nucleus	Nucleus subthalamicus
29.	Globus pallidus II	Globus pallidus II
30.	Claustrum	Claustrum
31.	Extreme capsule	Capsula extrema
32.	External capsule	Capsula externa
33.	Transcapsular caudatolenticular gray striae	Striae griseae caudatolenticulares transcapsulares
34.	Posterior lateral nucleus of thalamus	Nucleus lateralis posterior thalami
35.	Internal medullary lamina of thalamus	Lamina medullaris interna thalami
36.	Dorsal medial nucleus of thalamus	Nucleus medialis dorsalis thalami
37.	Body of fornix	Corpus fornicis
38.	Superior frontal gyrus	Gyrus frontalis superior

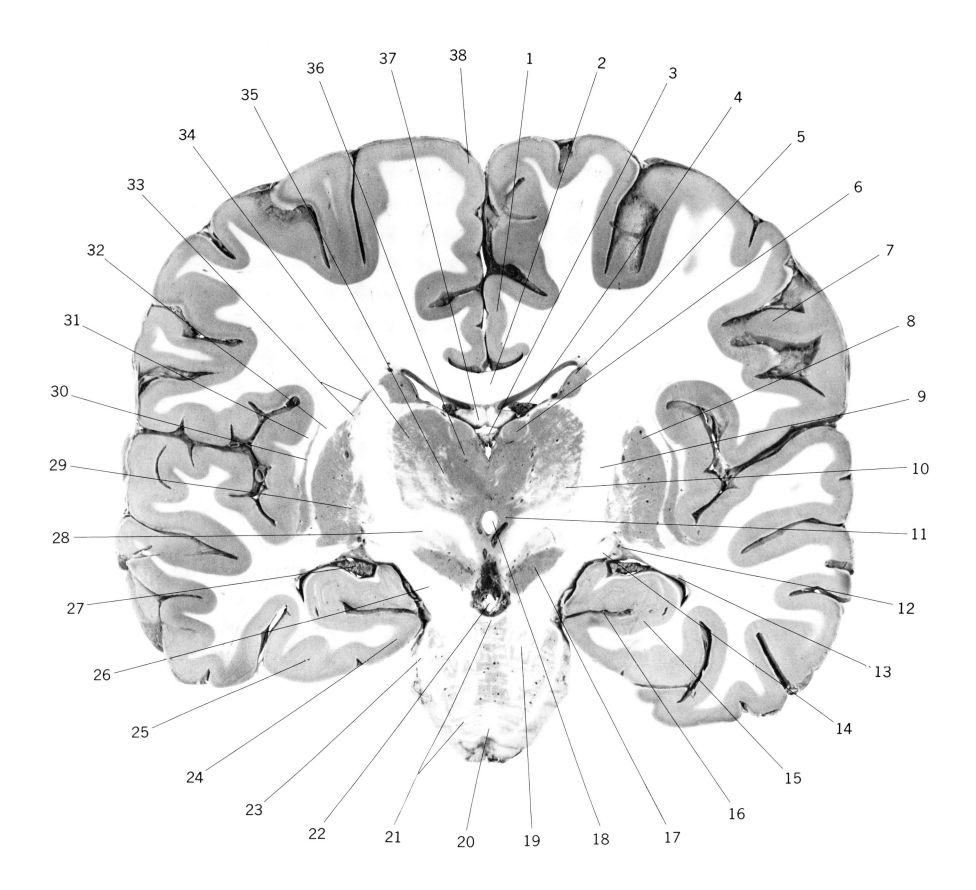

Posterior Surface of Coronal Section through Posterior Limit of Interpeduncular Fossa X1.5

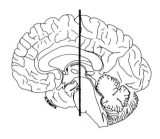

1.	Third ventricle	Ventriculus tertius
2.	Dorsal medial nucleus of thalamus	Nucleus medialis dorsalis thalami
3.	Body of lateral ventricle	Corpus ventriculi lateralis
4.	Rostal peduncle of thalamus	Pedunculus rostralis thalami
5.	Corona radiata	Corona radiata
6.	Posterior limb of internal capsule	Crus posterius capsulae internae
7.	Circular sulcus of insula	Sulcus circularis insulae
8.	Claustrum	Claustrum
9.	Centromedian nucleus of thalamus	Nucleus centromedianus thalami
10.	Medial longitudinal fasciculus	Fasciculus longitudinalis medialis
11.	Globus pallidus II	Globus pallidus II
12.	Optic radiations	Radiatio optica
13.	Tail of caudate nucleus	Cauda nuclei caudati
14.	Stria terminalis	Stria terminalis
15.	Optic tract	Tractus opticus
16.	Uncus	Uncus
17.	Cerebral peduncle	Pedunculus cerebri
18.	Red nucleus	Nucleus ruber
19.	Fasciculus retroflexus	Fasciculus retroflexus
20.	Medial nucleus of pons	Nucleus medialis pontis
21.	Interpeduncular fossa	Fossa interpeduncularis
22.	Middle cerebellar peduncle	Pedunculus cerebellaris medius
23.	Interpeduncular nucleus	Nucleus interpeduncularis
24.	Substantia nigra	Substantia nigra
25.	Posterior cerebral artery	Arteria cerebri posterior
26.	Hippocampus	Hippocampus
27.	Medullary lamina of red nucleus	Lamina medullaris nuclei rubris
28.	Medial lemniscus	Lemniscus medialis
29.	Posteromedial ventral nucleus of thalamus	Nucleus ventralis posteromedialis thalami
30.	Putamen	Putamen
31.	Posterolateral ventral nucleus of thalamus	Nucleus ventralis posterolateralis thalami
32.	Central sulcus	Sulcus centralis
33.	Posterior lateral nucleus of thalamus	Nucleus lateralis posterior thalami
34.	Tail of caudate nucleus	Cauda nuclei caudati
35.	Superior occipitofrontal fasciculus	Fasciculus occipitofrontalis superior
36.	Stria terminalis	Stria terminalis
37.	Lateral dorsal nucleus of thalamus	Nucleus lateralis dorsalis thalami
38.	Body of fornix	Corpus fornicis

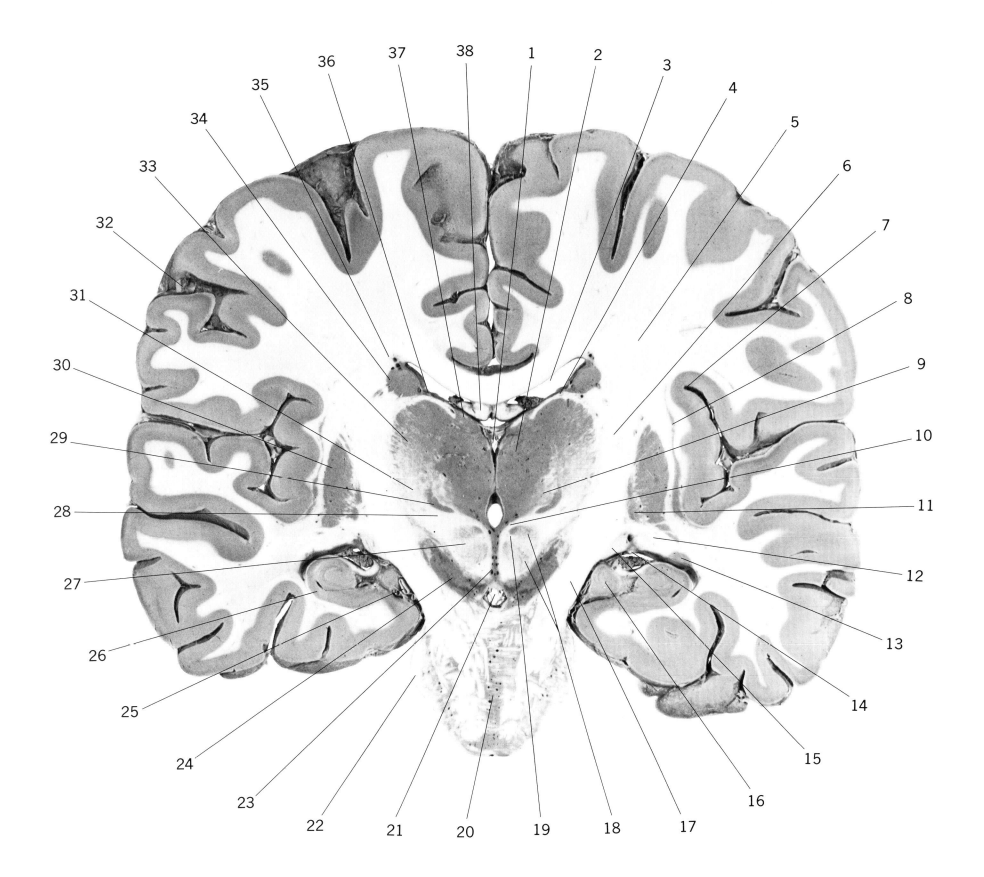

Posterior Surface of Coronal Section through Posterior Commissure X1.5

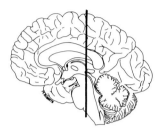

1.	Cingulum	Cingulum
2.	Crus of fornix	Crus fornicis
3.	Tail of caudate nucleus	Cauda nuclei caudati
4.	Third ventricle	Ventriculus tertius
5.	Posterior lateral nucleus of thalamus	Nucleus lateralis posterior thalami
6.	Posterior commissure	Commissura posterior
7.	Posterior limb of internal capsule	Crus posterius capsulae internae
8.	Cerebral aqueduct	Aqueductus cerebri
9.	Superior temporal gyrus	Gyrus temporalis superior
10.	Medial lemniscus	Lemniscus medialis
11.	Parahippocampal gyrus	Gyrus parahippocampalis
12.	Collateral sulcus	Sulcus collateralis
13.	Central tegmental tract	Tractus tegmentalis centralis
14.	Decussation of superior cerebellar peduncles	Decussatio pedunculorum cerebellarium superiorum
15.	Pontine nuclei	Nuclei pontis
16.	Raphe of pons	Raphe pontis
17.	Inferior olivary nucleus	Nucleus olivaris inferior
18.	Superior cerebellar peduncle	Pedunculus cerebellaris superior
19.	Middle cerebellar peduncle	Pedunculus cerebellaris medius
20.	Medial longitudinal fasciculus	Fasciculus longitudinalis medialis
21.	Lateral occipitotemporal gyrus	Gyrus occipitotemporalis lateralis
22.	Inferior temporal gyrus	Gyrus temporalis inferior
23.	Lateral lemniscus	Lemniscus lateralis
24.	Inferior horn of lateral ventricle	Cornu inferius ventriculi lateralis
25.	Alveus of hippocampus	Alveus hippocampi
26.	Tail of caudate nucleus	Cauda nuclei caudati
27.	Posterior cerebral artery	Arteria cerebri posterior
28.	Lateral geniculate body	Corpus geniculatum laterale
29.	Transcapsular caudatolenticular gray striae	Striae griseae caudatolenticulares transcapsulares
30.	Medial geniculate body	Corpus geniculatum mediale
31.	Rostral peduncle of thalamus	Pedunculus rostralis thalami
32.	Dorsal medial nucleus of thalamus	Nucleus medialis dorsalis thalami
33.	Fasciculus retroflexus	Fasciculus retroflexus
34.	Body of corpus callosum	Truncus corporis callosi

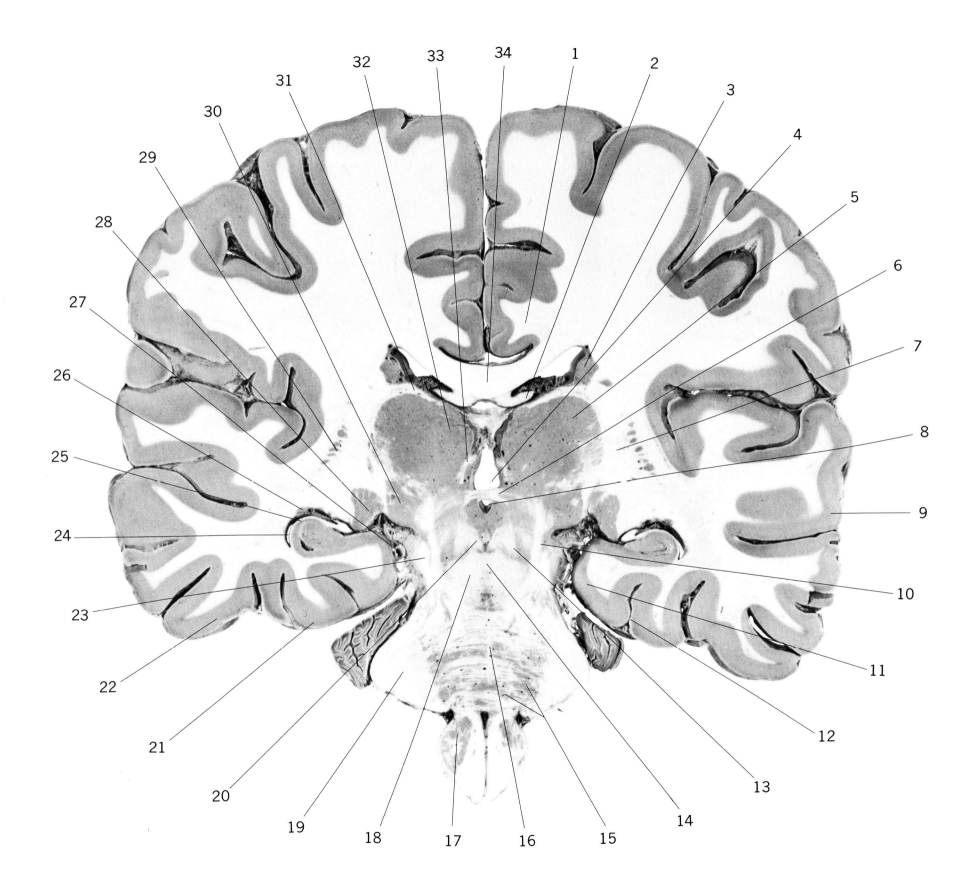

Anterior Surface of Coronal Section through Commissure of Superior Colliculi X1.5

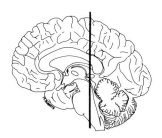

1. Commissure of fornix
2. Pineal gland
3. Body of lateral ventricle
4. Central sulcus
5. Commissure of superior colliculi
6. Transcapsular caudatolenticular gray striae
7. Brachium of superior colliculus
8. Triangular area
9. Lateral cerebral fissure
10. Superior temporal gyrus
11. Tail of caudate nucleus
12. Optic radiations
13. Middle temporal gyrus
14. Dentate gyrus
15. Hippocampus
16. Brachium of inferior colliculus
17. Superior cerebellar peduncle
18. Lateral recess of fourth ventricle
19. Rootlets of vagus nerve (X)
20. Inferior olivary nucleus
21. Cerebral aqueduct
22. Central tegmental tract
23. Glossopharyngeal nerve (IX)
24. Medial longitudinal fasciculus
25. Middle cerebellar peduncle
26. Lateral lemniscus
27. Lateral occipitotemporal gyrus
28. Collateral sulcus
29. Inferior temporal gyrus
30. Parahippocampal gyrus
31. Middle temporal gyrus
32. Inferior horn of lateral ventricle
33. Posterior cerebral artery
34. Posterior limb of internal capsule
35. Superior colliculus
36. External medullary lamina of thalamus
37. Reticular nucleus of thalamus
38. Tail of caudate nucleus
39. Choroid plexus of lateral ventricle
40. Crus of fornix
41. Velum interpositum

Commissura fornicis
Corpus pineale
Corpus ventriculi lateralis
Sulcus centralis
Commissura colliculi superioris
Striae griseae caudatolenticulares transcapsulares
Brachium colliculi superioris
Area triangularis
Fissura lateralis cerebri
Gyrus temporalis superior
Cauda nuclei caudati
Radiatio optica
Gyrus temporalis medius
Gyrus dentatus
Hippocampus
Brachium colliculi inferioris
Pedunculus cerebellaris superior
Recessus lateralis ventriculi quarti
Nervus vagus (X)
Nucleus olivaris inferior
Aqueductus cerebri
Fasciculus tegmentalis centralis
Nervus glossopharyngeus (IX)
Fasciculus longitudinalis medialis
Pedunculus cerebellaris medius
Lemniscus lateralis
Gyrus occipitotemporalis lateralis
Sulcus collateralis
Gyrus temporalis inferior
Gyrus parahippocampalis
Gyrus temporalis medius
Cornu inferius ventriculi lateralis
Arteria cerebri posterior
Crus posterius capsulae internae
Colliculus superior
Lamina medullaris externa thalami
Nucleus reticularis thalami
Cauda nuclei caudati
Plexus choroideus ventriculi lateralis
Crus fornicis
Velum interpositum

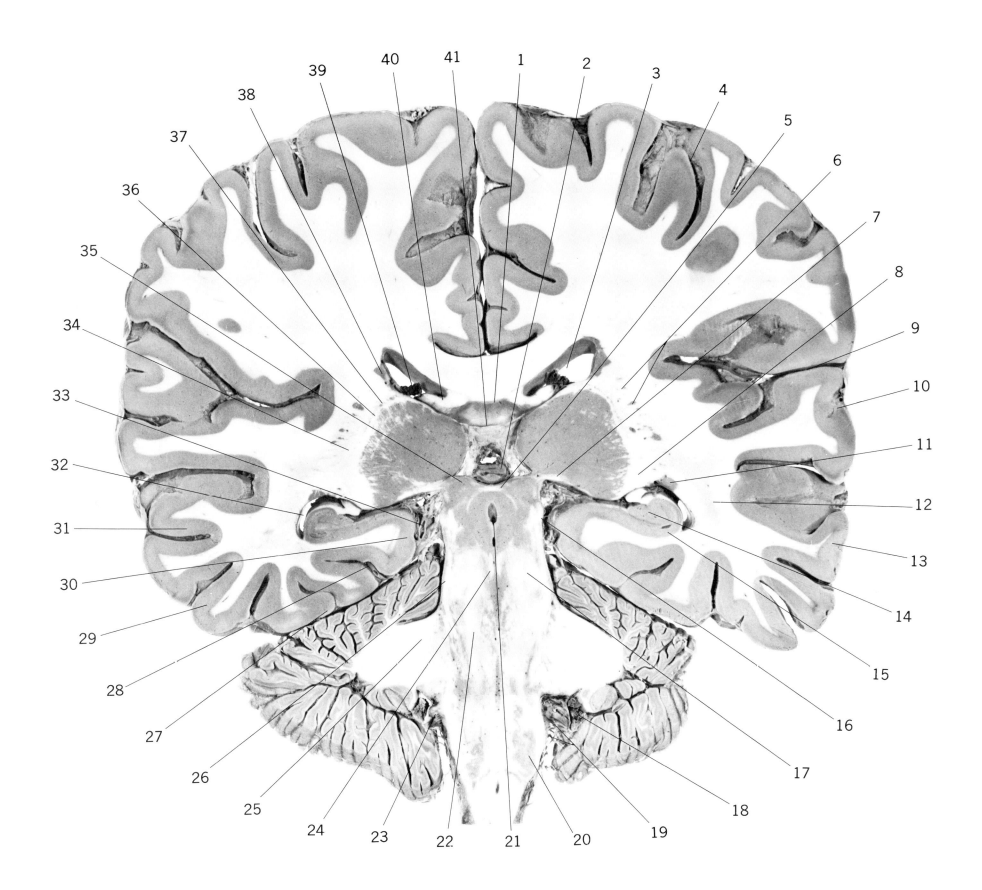

Posterior Surface of Coronal Section through Quadrigeminal Plate X1.5

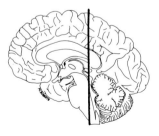

1. Velum interpositum — Velum interpositum
2. Internal cerebral vein — Vena cerebri interna
3. Choroid plexus of lateral ventricle — Plexus choroideus ventriculi lateralis
4. Choroidal fissure — Fissura choroidea
5. Tail of caudate nucleus — Cauda nuclei caudati
6. Pineal gland — Corpus pineale
7. Superior colliculus — Colliculus superior
8. Triangular area — Area triangularis
9. Fimbria hippocampus — Fimbria hippocampi
10. Alveus of hippocampus — Alveus hippocampi
11. Hippocampus — Hippocampus
12. Dentate gyrus — Gyrus dentatus
13. Brachium of inferior colliculus — Brachium colliculi inferioris
14. Inferior colliculus — Colliculus inferior
15. Commissure of inferior colliculi — Commissura colliculi inferioris
16. Uncinate fasciculus — Fasciculus uncinatus
17. Superior cerebellar peduncle — Pedunculus cerebellaris superior
18. Median sulcus — Sulcus medianus
19. Posterior spinocerebellar tract — Tractus spinocerebellaris posterior
20. Medial longitudinal fasciculus — Fasciculus longitudinalis medialis
21. Nucleus of abducens nerve (VI) — Nucleus nervi abducentis (VI)
22. Inferior cerebellar peduncle — Pedunculus cerebellaris inferior
23. Middle cerebellar peduncle — Pedunculus cerebellaris medius
24. Trochlear nerve (IV) — Nervus trochlearis (IV)
25. Collateral sulcus — Sulcus collateralis
26. Cingulum — Cingulum
27. Inferior horn of lateral ventricle — Cornu inferius ventriculi lateralis
28. Optic radiations — Radiatio optica
29. Tapetum — Tapetum
30. Tail of caudate nucleus — Cauda nuclei caudati
31. Retrolenticular part of internal capsule — Pars retrolenticularis capsulae internae
32. Lateral pulvinar nucleus of thalamus — Nucleus pulvinaris lateralis thalami
33. Transcapsular caudatolenticular gray striae — Striae griseae caudatolenticulares transcapsulares
34. Thalamostriate vein — Vena thalamostriata
35. Body of lateral ventricle — Corpus ventriculi lateralis
36. Crus of fornix — Crus fornicis
37. Medial pulvinar nucleus of thalamus — Nucleus pulvinaris medialis thalami
38. Splenium of corpus callosum — Splenium corporis callosi

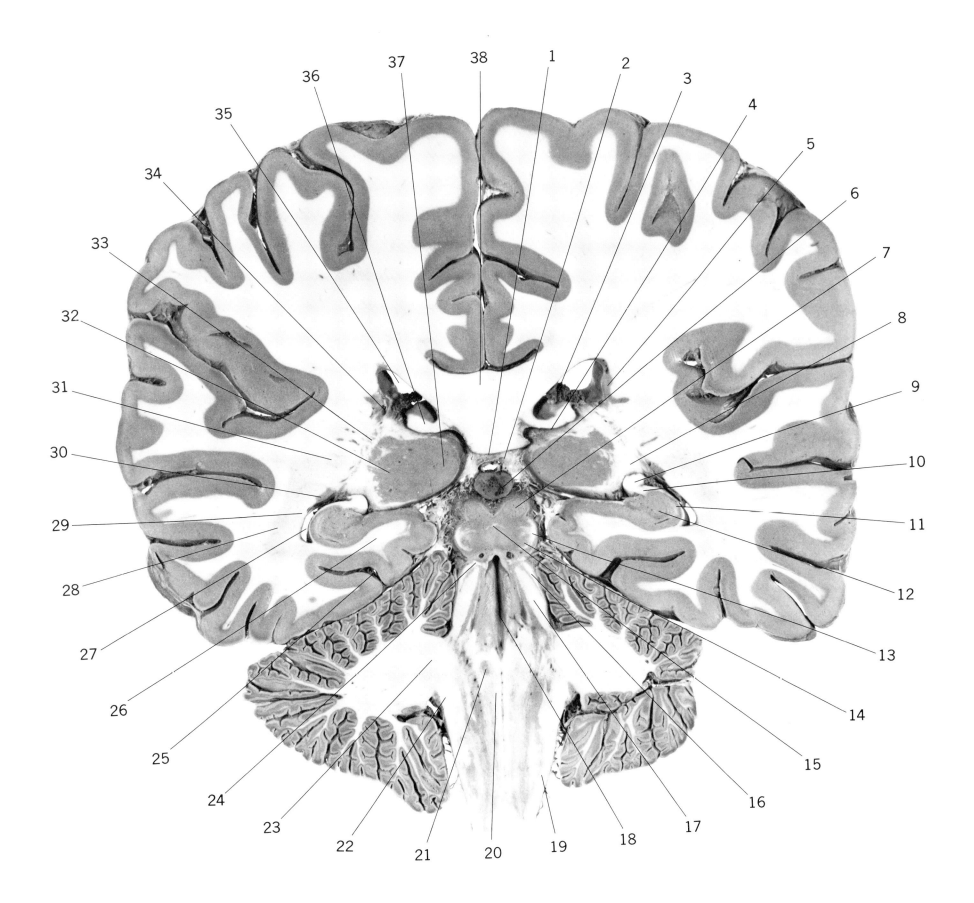

Posterior Surface of Coronal Section through Fourth Ventricle X1.5

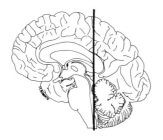

1. Sulcus of corpus callosum — Sulcus corporis callosi
2. Superior colliculus — Colliculus superior
3. Precentral gyrus — Gyrus precentralis
4. Postcentral gyrus — Gyrus postcentralis
5. Forceps major of corpus callosum — Forceps major corporis callosi
6. Atrium of lateral ventricle — Atrium ventriculi lateralis
7. Inferior parietal lobule — Lobulus parietalis inferior
8. Retrosplenial gyri of hippocampus — Gyri retrospleniales hippocampi
9. Tapetum — Tapetum
10. Optic radiations — Radiatio optica
11. Hippocampus — Hippocampus
12. Inferior longitudinal fasciculus — Fasciculus longitudinalis inferior
13. Lingual gyrus — Gyrus lingualis
14. Collateral sulcus — Sulcus collateralis
15. Middle cerebellar peduncle — Pedunculus cerebellaris medius
16. Fourth ventricle — Ventriculus quartus
17. Facial colliculus — Colliculus facialis
18. Sulcus limitans — Sulcus limitans
19. Hypoglossal trigone — Trigonum nervi hypoglossi
20. Vagal trigone — Trigonum nervi vagi
21. Striae medullares of fourth ventricle — Striae medullares ventriculi quarti
22. Lateral recess of fourth ventricle — Recessus lateralis ventriculi quarti
23. Superior medullary velum — Velum medullare superius
24. Superior cerebellar peduncle — Pedunculus cerebellaris superior
25. Central lobule — Lobulus centralis
26. Lateral occipitotemporal gyrus — Gyrus occipitotemporalis lateralis
27. Inferior colliculus — Colliculus inferior
28. Middle temporal gyrus — Gyrus temporalis medius
29. Anterior calcarine sulcus — Sulcus calcarinus anterior
30. Hippocampal sulcus — Sulcus hippocampi
31. Alveus of hippocampus — Alveus hippocampi
32. Choroid plexus of lateral ventricle — Plexus choroideus ventriculi lateralis
33. Tail of caudate nucleus — Cauda nuclei caudati
34. Crus of fornix — Crus fornicis
35. Pineal gland — Corpus pineale
36. Cingulum — Cingulum
37. Cingulate gyrus — Gyrus cinguli
38. Splenium of corpus callosum — Splenium corporis callosi

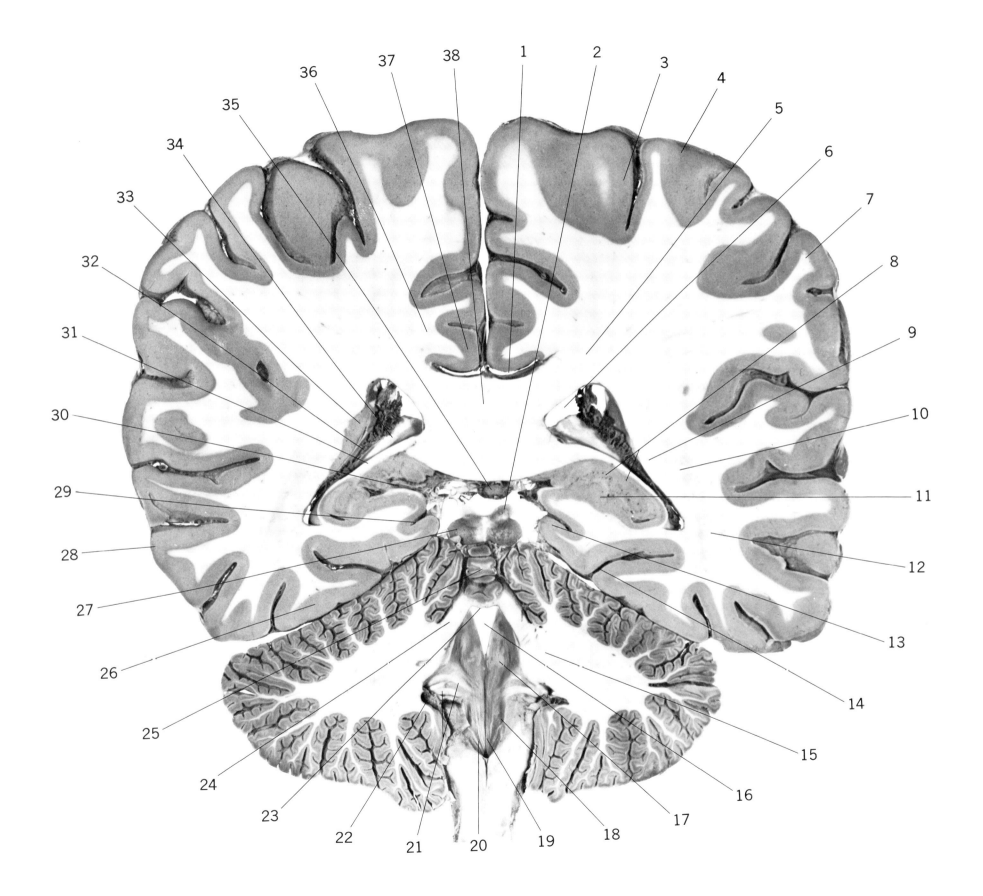

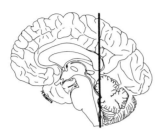

1.	Cingulate gyrus	Gyrus cinguli
2.	Indusium griseum	Indusium griseum
3.	Forceps major of corpus callosum	Forceps major corporis callosi
4.	Atrium of lateral ventricle	Atrium ventriculi lateralis
5.	Velum interpositum	Velum interpositum
6.	Tapetum	Tapetum
7.	Optic radiations	Radiatio optica
8.	Inferior longitudinal fasciculus	Fasciculus longitudinalis inferior
9.	Lingual gyrus	Gyrus lingualis
10.	Inferior temporal gyrus	Gyrus temporalis inferior
11.	Lateral occipitotemporal gyrus	Gyrus occipitotemporalis lateralis
12.	Anterior vermis of cerebellum	Vermis anterioris cerebelli
13.	Superior cerebellar peduncle	Pedunculus cerebellaris superior
14.	Superior medullary velum	Velum medullare superius
15.	Fourth ventricle	Ventriculus quartus
16.	Internal cerebral vein	Vena cerebri interna
17.	Dentate nucleus	Nucleus dentatus
18.	Anterior calcarine sulcus	Sulcus calcarinus anterior
19.	Cerebro-cerebellar fissure	Fissura cerebrocerebellaris
20.	Hippocampus	Hippocampus
21.	Inferior horn of lateral ventricle	Cornu inferius ventriculi lateralis
22.	Alveus of hippocampus	Alveus hippocampi
23.	Fimbria of hippocampus	Fimbria hippocampi
24.	Tail of caudate nucleus	Cauda nuclei caudati
25.	Choroid plexus of lateral ventricle	Plexus choroideus ventriculi laterali
26.	Splenium of corpus callosum	Splenium corporis callosi
27.	Cingulum	Cingulum
28.	Cingulate sulcus	Sulcus cinguli
29.	Longitudinal cerebral fissure	Fissura longitudinalis cerebri

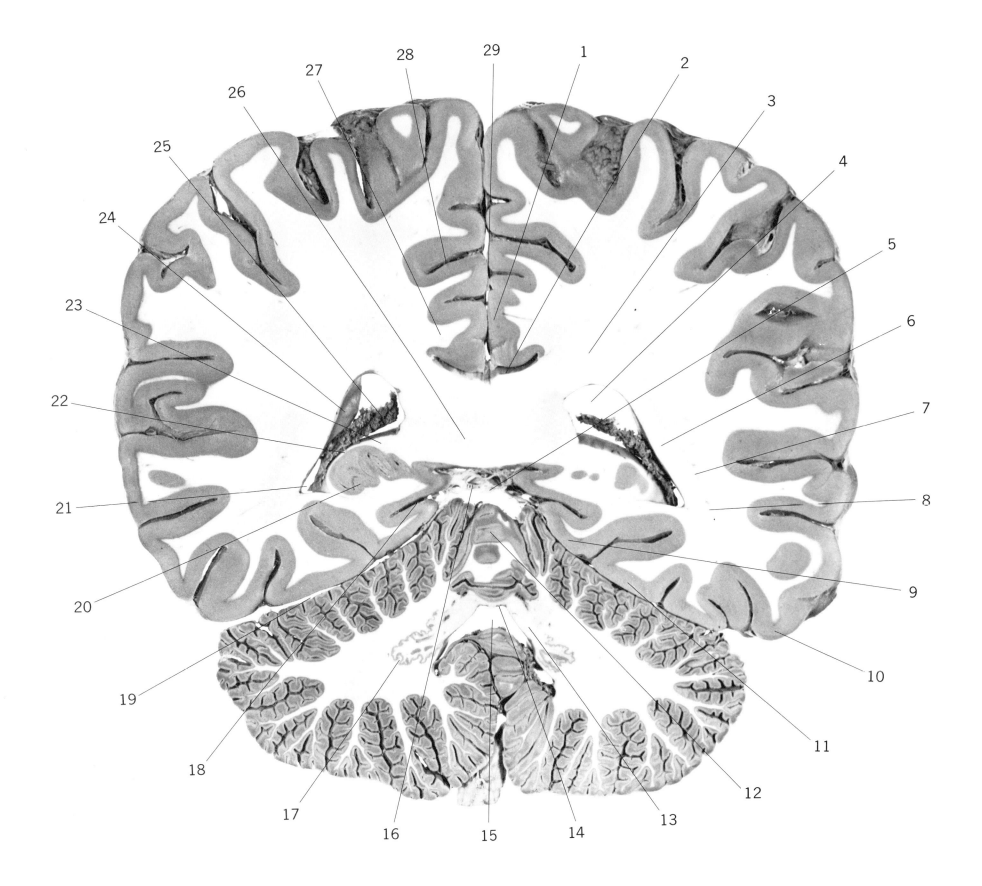

33

Anterior Surface of Coronal Section through
Posterior Horns of Lateral Ventricles X1.5

1.	Longitudinal cerebral fissure	Fissura longitudinalis cerebri
2.	Declive	Declive
3.	Radiations of corpus callosum	Radiatio corporis callosi
4.	Intraparietal sulcus	Sulcus intraparietalis
5.	Tapetum	Tapetum
6.	Inferior parietal gyrus	Gyrus parietalis inferior
7.	Posterior horn of lateral ventricle	Cornu posterius ventriculi lateralis
8.	Superior temporal gyrus	Gyrus temporalis superior
9.	Collateral sulcus	Sulcus collateralis
10.	Middle temporal gyrus	Gyrus temporalis medius
11.	Lateral occipitotemporal gyrus	Gyrus occipitotemporalis lateralis
12.	Inferior cerebellar decussation	Decussatio cerebellaris inferioris
13.	White laminae of cerebellum	Laminae albae cerebelli
14.	Dentate nucleus	Nucleus dentatus
15.	Secondary fissure	Fissura secunda
16.	Ventral paraflocculus	Paraflocculus ventralis
17.	Uvula	Uvula
18.	Pyramis	Pyramis
19.	Lamina alba of cerebellum	Lamina alba cerebelli
20.	Corpus medullare of cerebellum	Corpus medullare cerebelli
21.	Horizontal fissure	Fissura horizontalis
22.	Cerebro-cerebellar fissure	Fissura cerebrocerebellaris
23.	Inferior temporal gyrus	Gyrus temporalis inferior
24.	Inferior temporal sulcus	Sulcus temporalis inferior
25.	Lingual gyrus	Gyrus lingualis
26.	Collateral eminence	Eminentia collateralis
27.	Optic radiations	Radiatio optica
28.	Calcar avis	Calcar avis
29.	Calcarine sulcus	Sulcus calcarinus
30.	Culmen	Culmen
31.	Precuneus	Precuneus
32.	Superior parietal gyrus	Gyrus parietalis superior

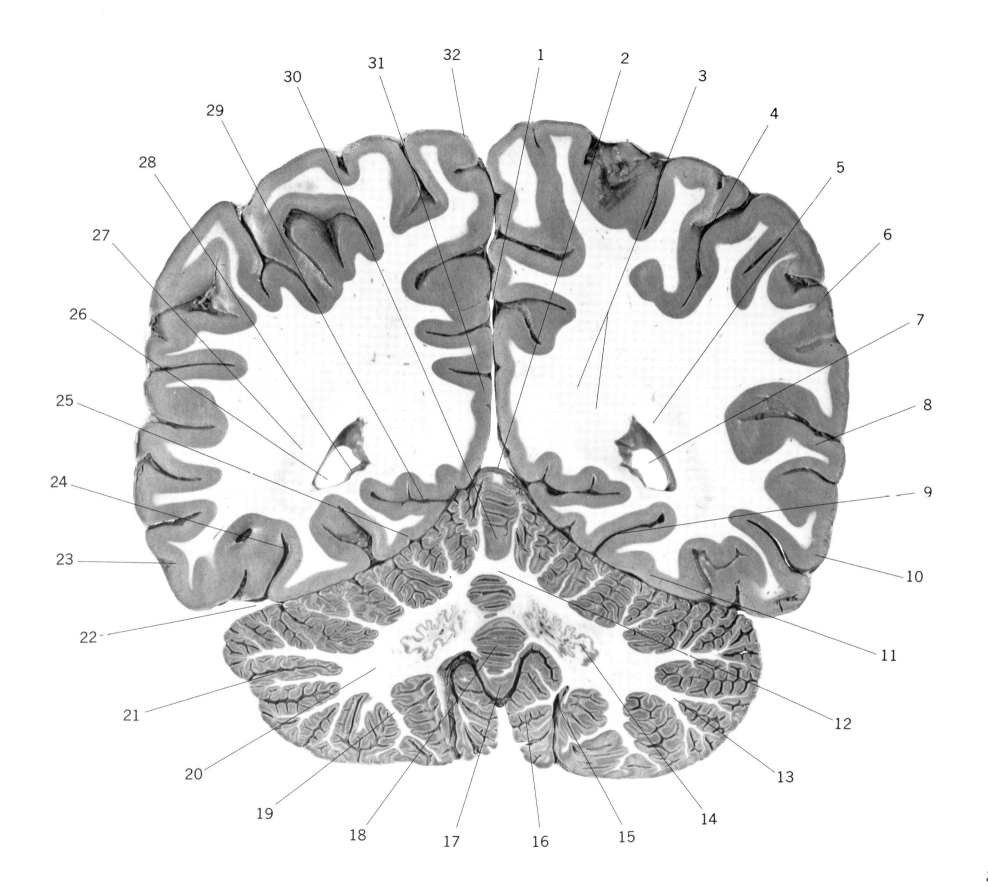

HORIZONTAL SECTIONS

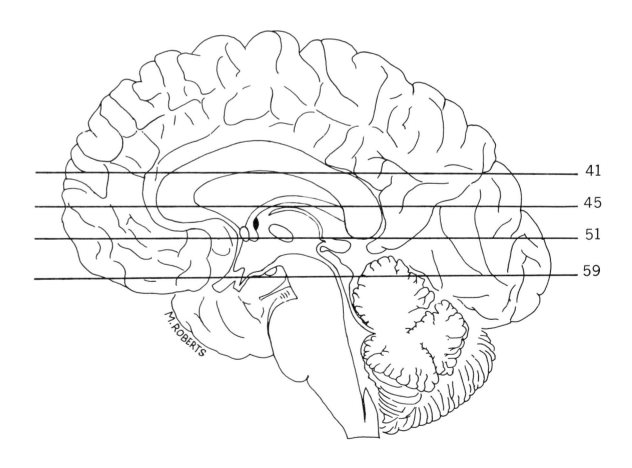

41

45

51

59

M.ROBERTS

Superior Surface of Horizontal Section through Superior Limit of Caudate Nucleus X1.4

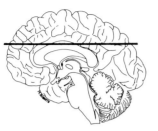

1. Atrium of lateral ventricle — Atrium ventriculi lateralis
2. Lateral cerebral fissure — Fissura lateralis cerebri
3. Angular gyrus — Gyrus angularis
4. Radiations of corpus callosum — Radiatio corporis callosi
5. Intraparietal sulcus — Sulcus intraparietalis
6. Cingulate sulcus — Sulcus cinguli
7. Parieto-occipital sulcus — Sulcus parietooccipitalis
8. Longitudinal cerebral fissure — Fissura longitudinalis cerebri
9. Cuneus — Cuneus
10. Medial parietal gyrus — Gyrus parietalis medialis
11. Cingulate gyrus — Gyrus cinguli
12. Superior temporal sulcus — Sulcus temporalis superior
13. Tail of caudate nucleus — Cauda nuclei caudati
14. Lateral cerebral fissure — Fissura lateralis cerebri
15. Thalamostriate vein — Vena thalamostriata
16. Postcentral gyrus — Gyrus postcentralis
17. Superior longitudinal fasciculus — Fasciculus longitudinalis superior
18. Precentral gyrus — Gyrus precentralis
19. Head of caudate nucleus — Caput nuclei caudati
20. Middle frontal gyrus — Gyrus frontalis medius
21. Cingulate gyrus — Gyrus cinguli
22. Superior frontal sulcus — Sulcus frontalis superior
23. Superior frontal gyrus — Gyrus frontalis superior
24. Cingulate sulcus — Sulcus cinguli
25. Cingulate gyrus — Gyrus cinguli
26. Pericallosal artery — Arteria pericallosa
27. Anterior horn of lateral ventricle — Cornu anterius ventriculi lateralis
28. Superior occipitofrontal fasciculus — Fasciculus occipitofrontalis superior
29. Body of corpus callosum — Truncus corpus callosi
30. Precentral sulcus — Sulcus precentralis
31. Corona radiata — Corona radiata
32. Central sulcus — Sulcus centralis

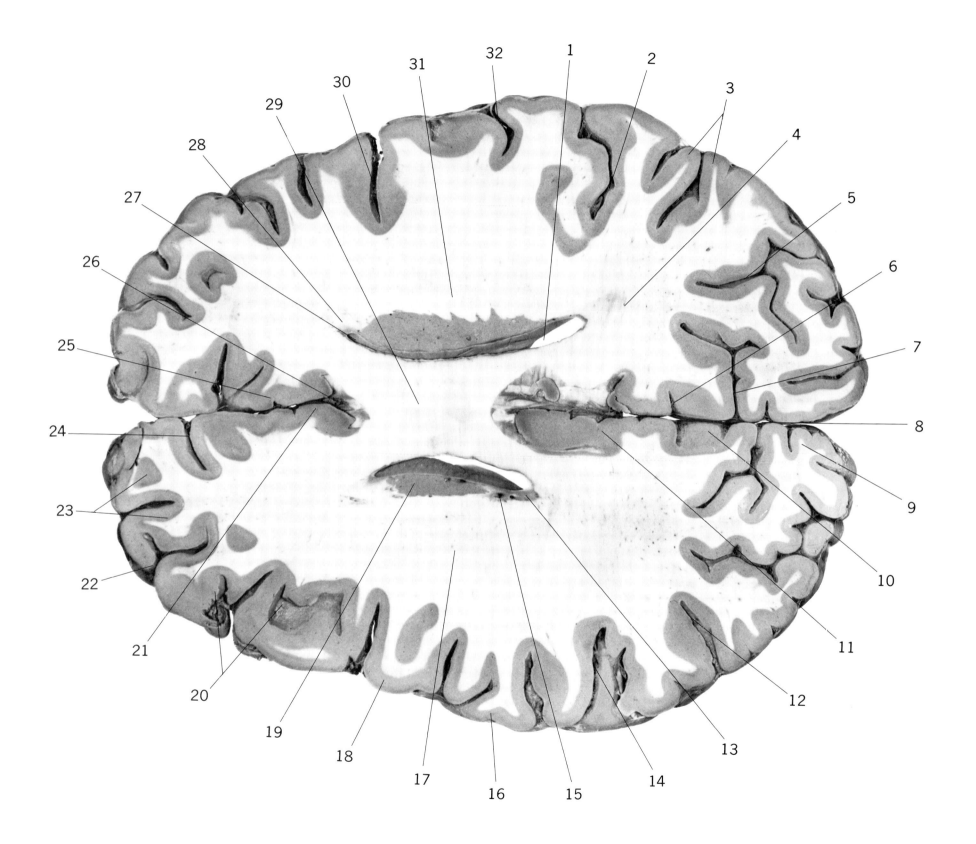

39

Superior Surface of Horizontal Section through Inferior Limit of Body of Corpus Callosum X1.4

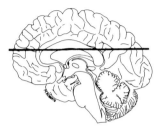

1. Superior longitudinal fasciculus — Fasciculus longitudinalis superior
2. Stratum zonale of thalamus — Stratum zonale thalami
3. Tail of caudate nucleus — Cauda nuclei caudati
4. Atrium of lateral ventricle — Atrium ventriculi lateralis
5. Splenium of corpus callosum — Splenium corporis callosi
6. Cingulate sulcus — Sulcus cinguli
7. Medial parietal gyrus — Gyrus parietalis medialis
8. Cuneus — Cuneus
9. Parieto-occipital sulcus — Sulcus parietooccipitalis
10. Intraparietal sulcus — Sulcus intraparietalis
11. Forceps major of corpus callosum — Forceps major corporis callosi
12. Choroidal vein — Vena choroidea
13. Crus of fornix — Crus fornicis
14. Thalamostriate vein — Vena thalamostriata
15. Lateral cerebral fissure — Fissura lateralis cerebri
16. Insula — Insula
17. Postcentral gyrus — Gyrus postcentralis
18. Central sulcus — Sulcus centralis
19. Corona radiata — Corona radiata
20. Precentral sulcus — Sulcus precentralis
21. Body of lateral ventricle — Corpus ventriculi lateralis
22. Superior occipitofrontal fasciculus — Fasciculus occipitofrontalis superior
23. Genu of corpus callosum — Genu corporis callosi
24. Cingulate gyrus — Gyrus cinguli
25. Indusium griseum — Indusium griseum
26. Longitudinal cerebral fissure — Fissura longitudinalis cerebri
27. Forceps minor of corpus callosum — Forceps minor corporis callosi
28. Anterior horn of lateral ventricle — Cornu anterius ventriculi lateralis
29. Head of caudate nucleus — Caput nuclei caudati
30. Choroid plexus of lateral ventricle — Plexus choroideus ventriculi lateralis
31. Transcapsular caudatolenticular gray striae — Striae griseae caudatolenticulares transcapsulares
32. Posterior lateral nucleus of thalamus — Nucleus lateralis posterior thalami
33. Posterior limb of internal capsule — Crus posterius capsulae internae
34. Insula — Insula

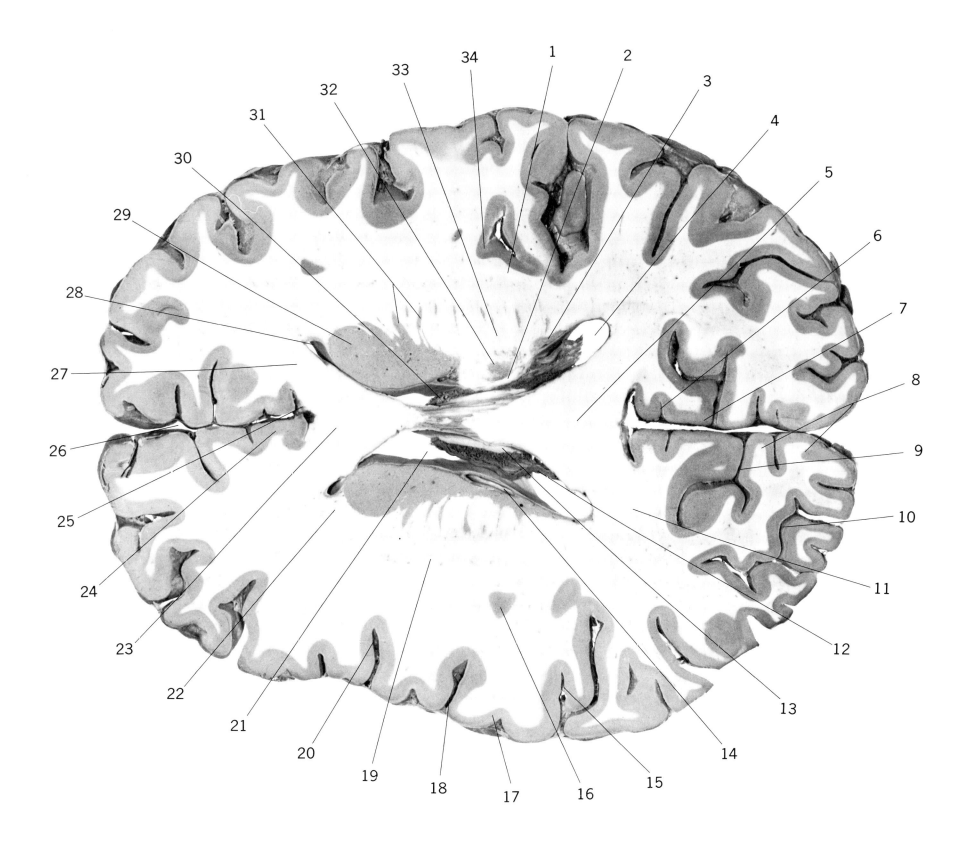

Inferior Surface of Horizontal Section through Dorsal Limit of Putamen X1.4

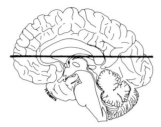

1.	Posterior lateral nucleus of thalamus	Nucleus lateralis posterior thalami
2.	Stratum zonale of thalamus	Stratum zonale thalami
3.	Tail of caudate nucleus	Cauda nuclei caudati
4.	Splenium of corpus callosum	Splenium corporis callosi
5.	Sulcus of corpus callosum	Sulcus corporis callosi
6.	Cingulate gyrus	Gyrus cinguli
7.	Parieto-occipital sulcus	Sulcus parietoocipitalis
8.	Cuneus	Cuneus
9.	Alveus of hippocampus	Alveus hippocampi
10.	Fimbria of hippocampus	Fimbria hippocampi
11.	Atrium of lateral ventricle	Atrium ventriculi lateralis
12.	Optic radiations	Radiatio optica
13.	Lateral dorsal nucleus of thalamus	Nucleus lateralis dorsalis thalami
14.	Internal medullary lamina of thalamus	Lamina medullaris interna thalami
15.	Insula	Insula
16.	Body of fornix	Corpus fornicis
17.	Posterior limb of internal capsule	Crus posterius capsulae internae
18.	Anteroventral nucleus of thalamus	Nucleus anteroventralis thalami
19.	Anterior limb of internal capsule	Crus anterius capsulae internae
20.	Body of fornix	Corpus fornicis
21.	Head of caudate nucleus	Caput nuclei caudati
22.	Lamina of septum pellucidum	Lamina septi pellucidi
23.	Cavum of septum pellucidum	Cavum septi pellucidi
24.	Cingulum	Cingulum
25.	Cingulate sulcus	Sulcus cinguli
26.	Genu of corpus callosum	Genu corporis callosi
27.	Anterior horn of lateral ventricle	Cornu anterius ventriculi lateralis
28.	Choroid plexus	Plexus choroideus
29.	Transcapsular caudatolenticular gray striae	Striae griseae caudatolenticulares transcapsulares
30.	Putamen	Putamen
31.	Extreme capsule	Capsula extrema
32.	External capsule	Capsula externa
33.	Claustrum	Claustrum
34.	Thalamostriate vein	Vena thalamostriata

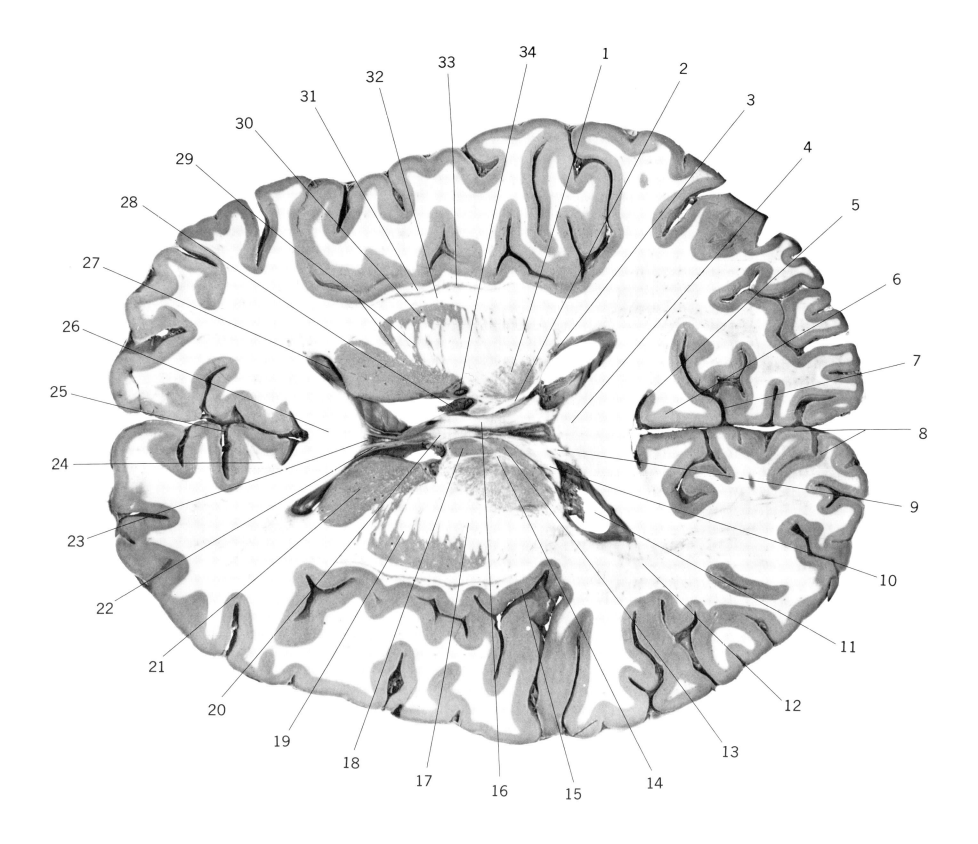

Superior Surface of Horizontal Section through Dorsal Limit of Putamen X1.4

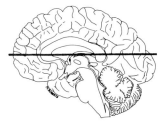

1. Anteroventral nucleus of thalamus — Nucleus anteroventralis thalami
2. Long gyrus of insula — Gyrus longus insulae
3. Posterior lateral nucleus of thalamus — Nucleus lateralis posterior thalami
4. Posterior limb of internal capsule — Crus posterius capsulae internae
5. Lateral pulvinar nucleus of thalamus — Nucleus pulvinaris lateralis thalami
6. Optic radiations — Radiatio optica
7. Forceps major of corpus callosum — Forceps major corporis callosi
8. Fimbria of hippocampus — Fimbria hippocampi
9. Cuneus — Cuneus
10. Parieto-occipital sulcus — Sulcus parietooccipitalis
11. Splenium of corpus callosum — Splenium corporis callosi
12. Alveus of hippocampus — Alveus hippocampi
13. Choroidal fissure — Fissura choroidea
14. Atrium of lateral ventricle — Atrium ventriculi lateralis
15. Choroid plexus of lateral ventricle — Plexus choroideus ventriculi lateralis
16. Tail of caudate nucleus — Cauda nuclei caudati
17. Parietal operculum — Operculum parietale
18. Lateral dorsal nucleus of thalamus — Nucleus lateralis dorsalis thalami
19. Internal medullary lamina of thalamus — Lamina medullaris interna thalami
20. Thalamostriate vein — Vena thalamostriata
21. Frontal operculum — Operculum frontale
22. Transcapsular caudatolenticular gray striae — Striae griseae caudatolenticulares transcapsulares
23. Circular sulcus of insula — Sulcus circularis insulae
24. Anterior horn of lateral ventricle — Cornu anterius ventriculi lateralis
25. Forceps minor of corpus callosum — Forceps minor corporis callosi
26. Lamina of septum pellucidum — Lamina septi pellucidi
27. Cingulate gyrus — Gyrus cinguli
28. Cingulate sulcus — Sulcus cinguli
29. Genu of corpus callosum — Genu corporis callosi
30. Cavum of septum pellucidum — Cavum septi pellucidi
31. Head of caudate nucleus — Caput nuclei caudati
32. Short gyri of insula — Gyri breves insulae
33. Genu of internal capsule — Genu capsulae internae
34. Putamen — Putamen
35. Precentral gyrus of insula — Gyrus precentralis insulae
36. Body of fornix — Corpus fornicis

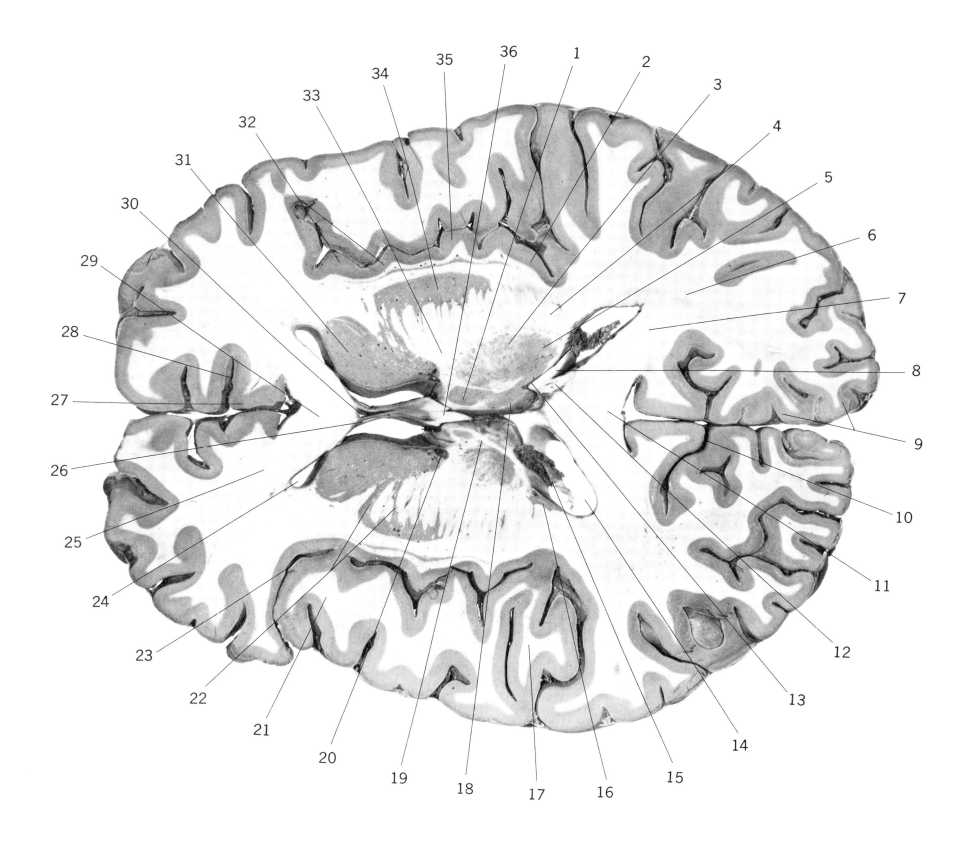

45

Superior Surface of Horizontal Section through Frontoparietal Opercula X1.4

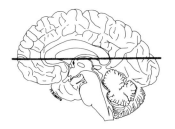

1. Long gyrus of insula — Gyrus longus insulae
2. Retrolenticular part of internal capsule — Pars retrolenticularis capsulae internae
3. Lateral pulvinar nucleus of thalamus — Nucleus pulvinaris lateralis thalami
4. Medial pulvinar nucleus of thalamus — Nucleus pulvinaris medialis thalami
5. Internal cerebral vein — Vena cerebri interna
6. Forceps major of corpus callosum — Forceps major corporis callosi
7. Dorsal medial nucleus of thalamus — Nucleus medialis dorsalis thalami
8. Splenium of corpus callosum — Splenium corporis callosi
9. Cuneus — Cuneus
10. Calcarine sulcus — Sulcus calcarinus
11. Alveus of hippocampus — Alveus hippocampi
12. Fimbria of hippocampus — Fimbria hippocampi
13. Choroid plexus of lateral ventricle — Plexus choroideus ventriculi lateralis
14. Tapetum — Tapetum
15. Tail of caudate nucleus — Cauda nuclei caudati
16. Posterior limb of internal capsule — Crus posterius capsulae internae
17. Circular sulcus of insula — Sulcus circularis insulae
18. Internal medullary lamina of thalamus — Lamina medullaris interna thalami
19. Parietal operculum — Operculum parietale
20. Genu of internal capsule — Genu capsulae internae
21. Column of fornix — Columna fornicis
22. Frontal operculum — Operculum frontale
23. Anterior horn of lateral ventricle — Cornu anterius ventriculi lateralis
24. Septum pellucidum — Septum pellucidum
25. Cavum of septum pellucidum — Cavum septi pellucidi
26. Forceps minor of corpus callosum — Forceps minor corporis callosi
27. Genu of corpus callosum — Genu corporis callosi
28. Cingulate gyrus — Gyrus cinguli
29. Rostral peduncle of thalamus — Pedunculus rostralis thalami
30. Head of caudate nucleus — Caput nuclei caudati
31. Superior occipitofrontal fasciculus — Fasciculus occipitofrontalis superior
32. Thalamostriate vein — Vena thalamostriata
33. Anteroventral nucleus of thalamus — Nucleus anteroventralis thalami
34. Short gyrus of insula — Gyrus brevus insulae
35. Putamen — Putamen
36. Anterior ventral nucleus of thalamus — Nucleus ventralis anterior thalami
37. Long gyrus of insula — Gyrus longus insulae
38. Posterior lateral nucleus of thalamus — Nucleus lateralis posterior thalami

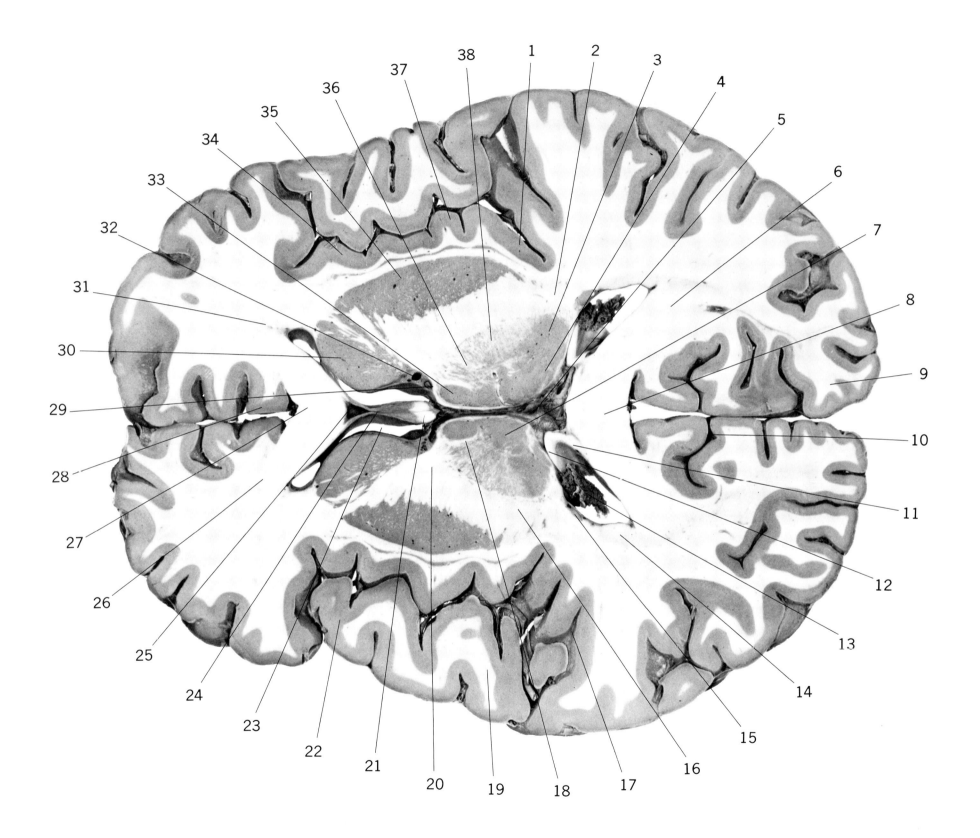

Superior Surface of Horizontal Section through Mid-level of Diencephalon X1.4

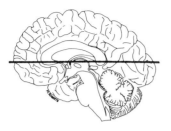

1. Putamen — Putamen
2. Posterior limb of internal capsule — Crus posterius capsulae internae
3. Posterolateral ventral nucleus of thalami — Nucleus ventralis posterolateralis thalami
4. Choroid plexus of lateral ventricle — Plexus choroideus ventriculi lateralis
5. Optic radiations — Radiatio optica
6. Centromedian nucleus of thalamus — Nucleus centromedianus thalami
7. Lateral pulvinar nucleus of thalamus — Nucleus pulvinaris lateralis thalami
8. Medial pulvinar nucleus of thalamus — Nucleus pulvinaris medialis thalami
9. Stria medullaris of thalamus — Stria medullaris thalami
10. Cuneus — Cuneus
11. Cingulate gyrus — Gyrus cinguli
12. Splenium of corpus callosum — Splenium corporis callosi
13. Tapetum — Tapetum
14. Atrium of lateral ventricle — Atrium ventriculi lateralis
15. Fimbria of hippocampus — Fimbria hippocampi
16. Tail of caudate nucleus — Cauda nuclei caudati
17. Circular sulcus of insula — Sulcus circularis insulae
18. Dorsal medial nucleus of thalamus — Nucleus medialis dorsalis thalami
19. Long gyrus of insula — Gyrus longus insulae
20. Mamillothalamic fasciculus — Fasciculus mamillothalamicus
21. Precentral gyrus of insula — Gyrus precentralis insulae
22. Short gyri of insula — Gyri breves insulae
23. Third ventricle — Ventriculus tertius
24. Column of fornix — Columna fornicis
25. Head of caudate nucleus — Caput nuclei caudati
26. Genu of corpus callosum — Genu corporis callosi
27. Stylus of septum pellucidum — Stylus septi pellucidi
28. Pericallosal artery — Arteria pericallosa
29. Stria medullaris of thalamus — Stria medullaris thalami
30. Genu of internal capsule — Genu capsulae internae
31. Anterior limb of internal capsule — Crus anterius capsulae internae
32. Globus pallidus II — Globus pallidus II
33. Extreme capsule — Capsula extrema
34. External medullary lamina of globus pallidus — Lamina medullaris externa pallidi
35. Claustrum — Claustrum
36. External capsule — Capsula externa

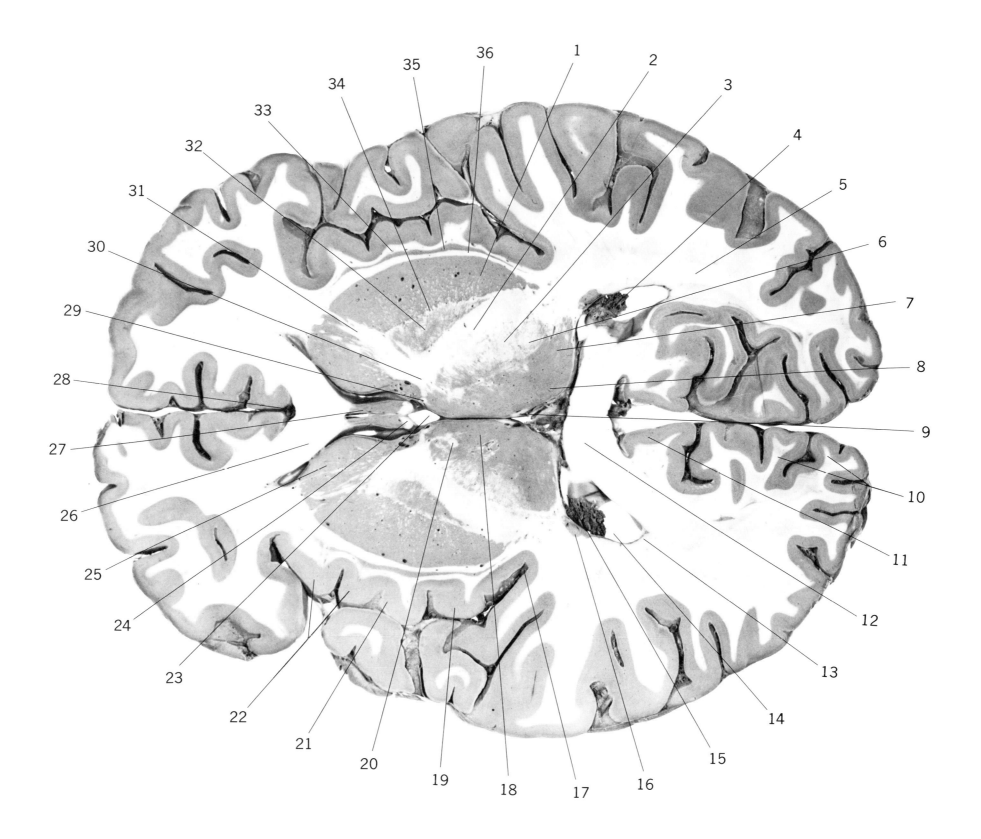

Inferior Surface of Horizontal Section through
Anterior Commissure X1.4

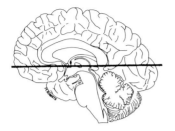

1.	Circular sulcus of insula	Sulcus circularis insulae
2.	Lateral ventral nucleus of thalamus	Nucleus ventralis lateralis thalami
3.	Dorsal medial nucleus of thalamus	Nucleus medialis dorsalis thalami
4.	Tail of caudate nucleus	Cauda nuclei caudati
5.	Fimbria of hippocampus	Fimbria hippocampi
6.	Tapetum	Tapetum
7.	Optic radiations	Radiato optica
8.	Retrosplenial gyrus of hippocampus	Gyrus retrosplenialis hippocampi
9.	Stria medullaris of thalamus	Stria medullaris thalami
10.	Longitudinal cerebral fissure	Fissura longitudinalis cerebri
11.	Great cerebral vein	Vena cerebri magna
12.	Medial pulvinar nucleus of thalamus	Nucleus pulvinaris medialis thalami
13.	Choroidal fissure	Fissura choroidea
14.	Lateral pulvinar nucleus of thalamus	Nucleus pulvinaris lateralis thalami
15.	Choroid plexus of lateral ventricle	Plexus choroideus ventriculi lateralis
16.	Triangular area	Area triangularis
17.	Retrolenticular part of internal capsule	Pars retrolenticularis capsulae internae
18.	Mamillothalamic fasciculus	Fasciculus mamillothalamicus
19.	Branch of middle cerebral artery	Ramus arteriae cerebralis mediae
20.	Posterior limb of internal capsule	Crus posterius capsulae internae
21.	Long gyrus of insula	Gyrus longus insulae
22.	Globus pallidus I	Globus pallidus I
23.	Short gyri of insula	Gyri breves insulae
24.	Globus pallidus II	Globus pallidus II
25.	Internal medullary lamina of globus pallidus	Lamina medullaris interna pallidi
26.	Anterior limb of internal capsule	Crus anterius capsulae internae
27.	Lateral preoptic nucleus	Nucleus preopticus lateralis
28.	Column of fornix	Columna fornicis
29.	Cingulate gyrus	Gyrus cinguli
30.	Anterior commissure	Commissura anterior
31.	Third ventricle	Ventriculus tertius
32.	Head of caudate nucleus	Caput nuclei caudati
33.	Putamen	Putamen
34.	Paraventricular nucleus of hypothalamus	Nucleus paraventricularis hypothalami
35.	Lateral cerebral fissure	Fissura lateralis cerebri
36.	External medullary lamina of globus pallidus	Lamina medullaris externa pallidi
37.	Temporal operculum	Operculum temporale
38.	Interthalamic adhesion	Adhesio interthalamica

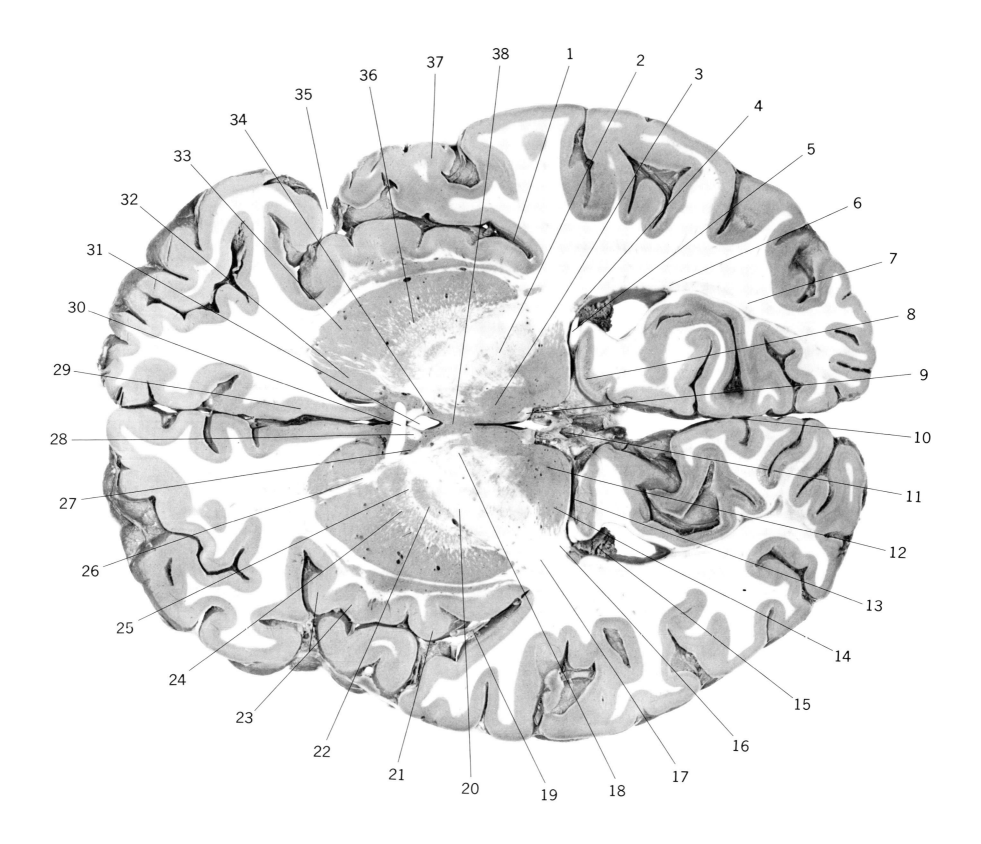

Inferior Surface of Horizontal Section through Habenular Commissure X1.4

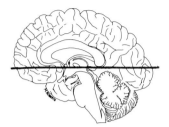

1.	Centromedian nucleus of thalamus	Nucleus centromedianus thalami
2.	Tail of caudate nucleus	Cauda nuclei caudati
3.	Lateral habenular nucleus	Nucleus habenularis lateralis
4.	Inferior longitudinal fasciculus	Fasciculus longitudinalis inferior
5.	Hippocampus	Hippocampus
6.	Posterior horn of lateral ventricle	Cornu posterius ventriculi lateralis
7.	Radiations of corpus callosum	Radiatio corporis callosi
8.	Medial pulvinar nucleus of thalamus	Nucleus pulvinaris medialis thalami
9.	Habenular commissure	Commissura habenularum
10.	Pineal gland	Corpus pineale
11.	Fasciculus retroflexus	Fasciculus retroflexus
12.	Stratum zonale of thalamus	Stratum zonale thalami
13.	Posterolateral ventral nucleus of thalamus	Nucleus ventralis posterolateralis thalami
14.	Choroid plexus of lateral ventricle	Plexus choroideus ventriculi lateralis
15.	Tapetum	Tapetum
16.	Alveus of hippocampus	Alveus hippocampi
17.	Fimbria of hippocampus	Fimbria hippocampi
18.	Stria terminalis	Stria terminalis
19.	Lateral pulvinar nucleus of thalamus	Nucleus pulvinaris lateralis thalami
20.	Ventrocaudal thalamic peduncle	Pedunculus ventrocaudalis thalami
21.	Posteromedial ventral nucleus of thalamus	Nucleus ventralis posteromedialis thalami
22.	Globus pallidus I and II	Globus pallidus I et II
23.	Claustrum	Claustrum
24.	Short gyri of insula	Gyri breves insulae
25.	Circular sulcus of insula	Sulcus circularis insulae
26.	Putamen	Putamen
27.	Anterior commissure	Commissura anterior
28.	Head of caudate nucleus	Caput nuclei caudati
29.	Mamillothalamic fasciculus	Fasciculus mamillothalamicus
30.	Third ventricle	Ventriculus tertius
31.	Column of fornix	Columna fornicis
32.	Tegmental area H_2	Area tegmentalis H_2
33.	Zona incerta	Zona incerta
34.	Internal medullary lamina of globus pallidus	Lamina medullaris interna pallidi
35.	Posterior limb of internal capsule	Crus posterius capsulae internae
36.	External medullary lamina of globus pallidus	Lamina medullaris externa pallidi
37.	Medial habenular nucleus	Nucleus habenularis medialis

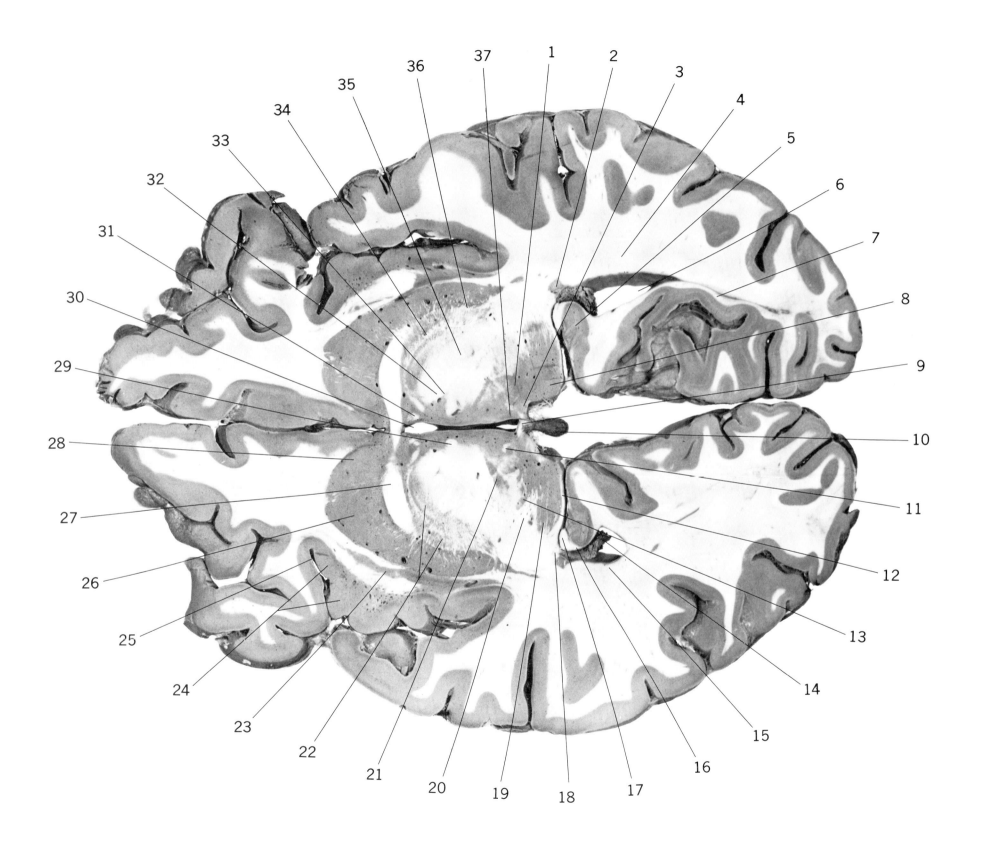

Inferior Surface of Horizontal Section through
Superior Colliculi X1.4

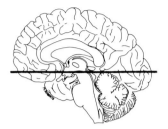

1.	Tail of caudate nucleus	Cauda nuclei caudati
2.	Fimbria of hippocampus	Fimbria hippocampi
3.	Lateral pulvinar nucleus of thalamus	Nucleus pulvinaris lateralis thalami
4.	Brachium of superior colliculus	Brachium colliculi superioris
5.	Cerebral aqueduct	Aqueductus cerebri
6.	Commissure of superior colliculi	Commissura colliculi superioris
7.	Vermis of cerebellum	Vermis cerebelli
8.	Anulus of cerebral aqueduct	Anulus aqueductus cerebri
9.	Superior colliculus	Colliculus superior
10.	Fasciculus retroflexus	Fasciculus retroflexus
11.	Capsule of medial geniculate body	Capsula corporis geniculati medialis
12.	Medial geniculate body	Corpus geniculatum mediale
13.	Middle temporal sulcus	Sulcus temporalis medius
14.	Dentate gyrus	Gyrus dentatus
15.	Alveus of hippocampus	Alveus hippocampi
16.	Stria terminalis	Stria terminalis
17.	Middle temporal gyrus	Gyrus temporalis medius
18.	Pregeniculate nucleus	Nucleus pregeniculatum
19.	Claustrum	Claustrum
20.	Superior temporal gyrus	Gyrus temporalis superior
21.	Anterior commissure	Commissure anterior
22.	Caudal nucleus of zona incerta	Nuclei zona incertae caudalis
23.	Posterior limb of internal capsule	Crus posterius capsulae internae
24.	Zona incerta	Zona incerta
25.	Red nucleus	Nucleus ruber
26.	Mamillothalamic fasciculus	Fasciculus mamillothalamicus
27.	Column of fornix	Columna fornicis
28.	Head of caudate nucleus	Caput nuclei caudati
29.	Ansa lenticularis	Ansa lenticularis
30.	Putamen	Putamen
31.	Globus pallidus	Globus pallidus
32.	Subthalamic nucleus	Nucleus subthalamicus
33.	Capsule of red nucleus	Capsula nuclei rubris
34.	Lateral geniculate body	Corpus geniculatum laterale

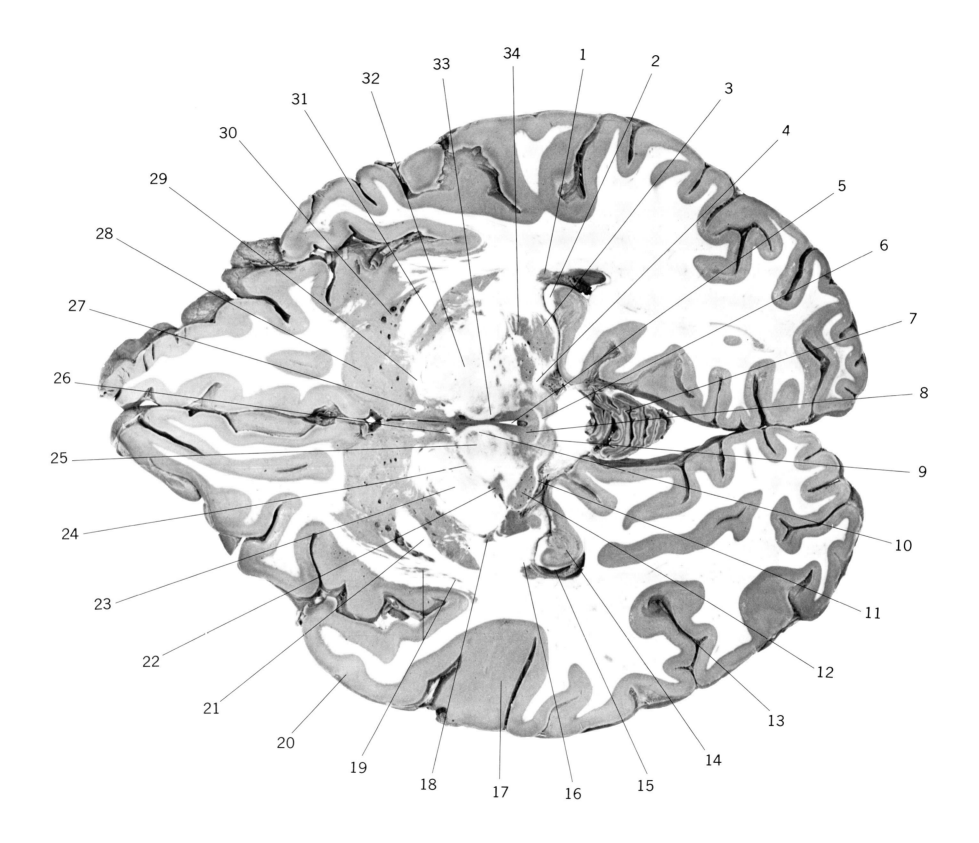

Inferior Surface of Horizontal Section through
Anterior Perforated Substance X1.4

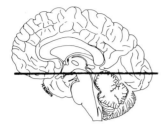

1.	Inferior horn of lateral ventricle	Cornu inferius ventriculi lateralis
2.	Choroid plexus of inferior horn of lateral ventricle	Plexus choroideus ventriculi lateralis cornu inferius
3.	Medial geniculate body	Corpus geniculatum mediale
4.	Red nucleus	Nucleus ruber
5.	Medial longitudinal fasciculus	Fasciculus longitudinalis medialis
6.	Superior colliculus	Colliculus superior
7.	Anulus of cerebral aqueduct	Anulus aqueductus cerebri
8.	Superior cistern	Cisterna superior
9.	Tegmental reticular formation	Formatio reticularis tegmentalis
10.	Substantia nigra	Substantia nigra
11.	Cerebral peduncle	Pedunculus cerebri
12.	Dentate gyrus	Gyrus dentatus
13.	Tapetum	Tapetum
14.	Hippocampus	Hippocampus
15.	Fimbria of hippocampus	Fimbria hippocampi
16.	Mamillary body	Corpus mamillare
17.	Principal mamillary fasciculus	Fasciculus mamillaris princeps
18.	Branch of middle cerebral artery	Ramus arteriae cerebralis mediae
19.	Lateral cerebral fissure	Fissura lateralis cerebri
20.	Optic tract	Tractus opticus
21.	Tuber cinereum	Tuber cinereum
22.	Medial orbital gyrus	Gyrus orbitalis medialis
23.	Straight gyrus	Gyrus rectus
24.	Anterior cerebral artery	Arteria cerebri anterior
25.	Anterior perforated substance	Substantia perforata anterior
26.	Mamillothalamic fasciculus	Fasciculus mamillothalamicus
27.	Uncus	Uncus
28.	Amygdala	Corpus amygdaloideum
29.	Anterior commissure	Commissura anterior
30.	Lateral geniculate body	Corpus geniculatum laterale
31.	Tail of caudate nucleus	Cauda nuclei caudati
32.	Alveus of hippocampus	Alveus hippocampi

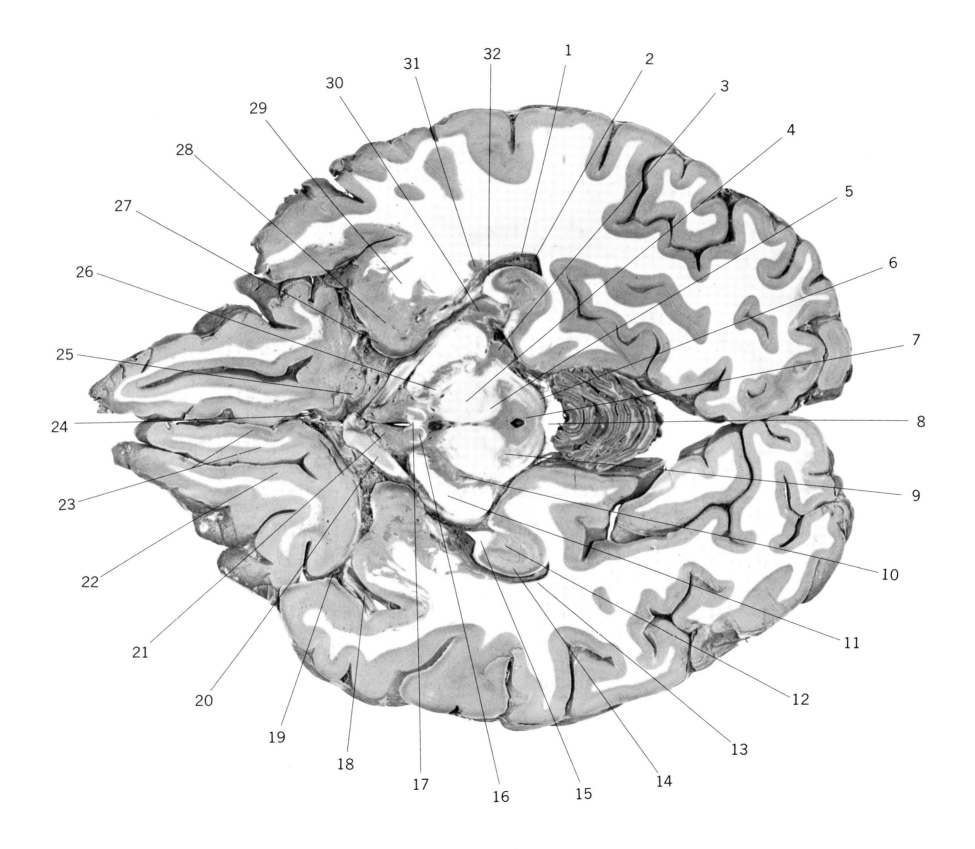

Inferior Surface of Horizontal Section through
Inferior Colliculi X1.4

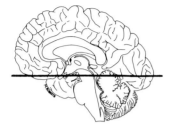

1.	Parahippocampal gyrus	Gyrus parahippocampalis
2.	Lateral lemniscus	Lemniscus lateralis
3.	Cristerna ambiens	Cisterna ambiens
4.	Brachium of inferior colliculus	Brachium colliculi inferioris
5.	Cerebral aqueduct	Aqueductus cerebri
6.	Vermis of cerebellum	Vermis cerebelli
7.	Calcarine sulcus	Sulcus calcarinus
8.	Anulus of cerebral aqueduct	Anulus aqueductus cerebri
9.	Inferior colliculus	Colliculus inferior
10.	Medial lemniscus	Lemniscus medialis
11.	Substantia nigra	Substantia nigra
12.	Frontopontine tract	Tractus frontopontinus
13.	Parietotemporo-occipitopontine tract	Tractus parietotemporo-occipitopontinus
14.	Dentate gyrus	Gyrus dentatus
15.	Hippocampus	Hippocampus
16.	Mamillary body	Corpus mamillare
17.	Alveus of hippocampus	Alveus hippocampi
18.	Anterior commissure	Commissura anterior
19.	Amygdala	Corpus amygdaloideum
20.	Infundibulum	Infundibulum
21.	Optic chiasm	Chiasma opticum
22.	Anterior cerebral artery	Arteria cerebri anterior
23.	Olfactory sulcus	Sulcus olfactorius
24.	Straight gyrus	Gyrus rectus
25.	Medial orbital gyrus	Gyrus orbitalis medialis
26.	Olfactory tract	Tractus olfactorius
27.	Optic tract	Tractus opticus
28.	Temporal pole	Polus temporalis
29.	Interpeduncular fossa	Fossa interpeduncularis
30.	Corticospinal tract	Tractus corticospinalis
31.	Superior cerebellar peduncle	Pedunculus cerebellaris superior
32.	Medial longitudinal fasciculus	Fasciculus longitudinalis medialis

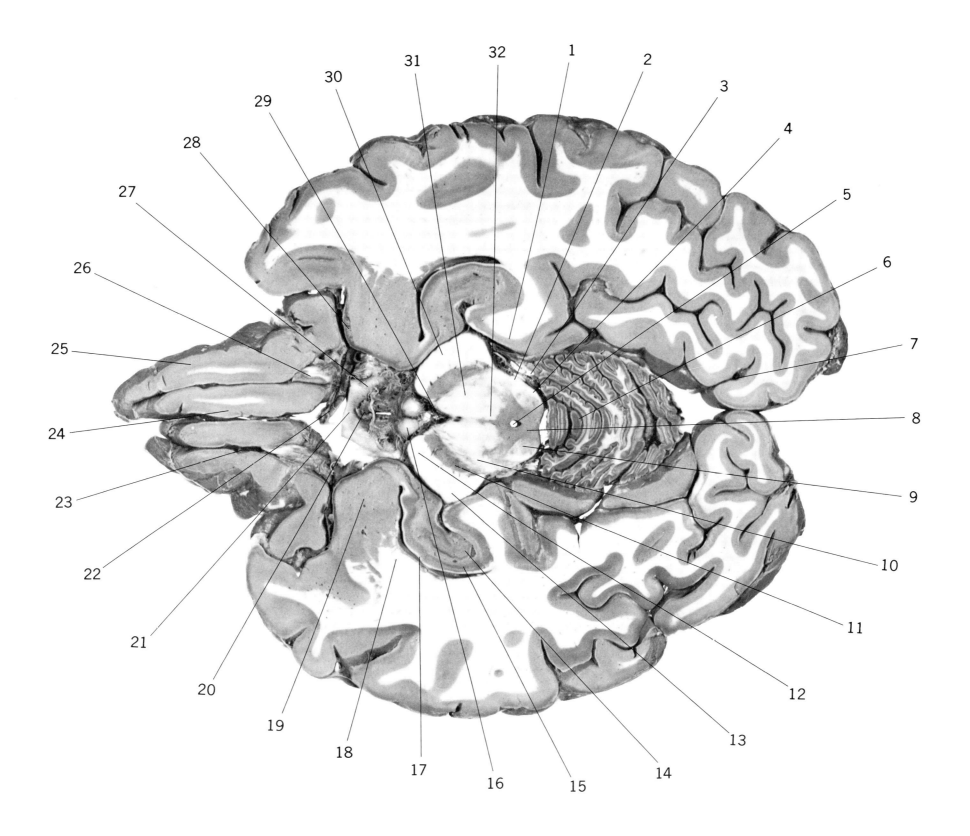

SAGITTAL SECTIONS

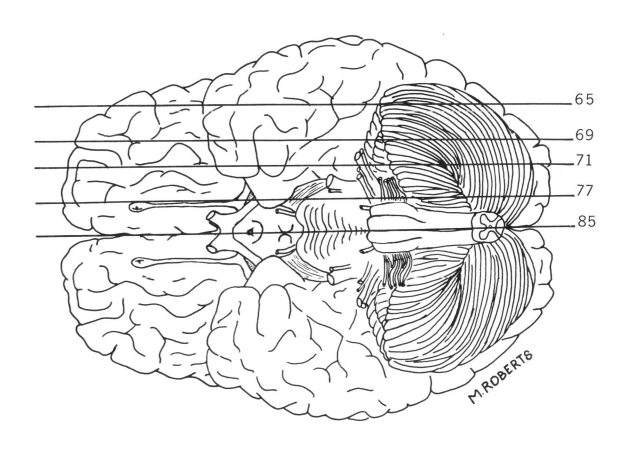

65

69

71

77

85

M.ROBERTS

Lateral Surface of Sagittal Section through Superior, Middle, and Inferior Temporal Gyri X1.4

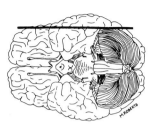

1.	Postcentral gyrus	Gyrus postcentralis
2.	Postcentral sulcus	Sulcus postcentralis
3.	Supermarginal gyrus	Gyrus supramarginalis
4.	Posterior ascending limb of lateral fissure	Ramus posterior ascendens fissurae lateralis
5.	Angular gyrus	Gyrus angularis
6.	Superior temporal sulcus	Sulcus temporalis superior
7.	Occipital gyri	Gyri occipitales
8.	Preoccipital notch	Incisura preoccipitalis
9.	Inferior temporal gyrus	Gyrus temporalis inferior
10.	Lateral cerebral fissure	Fissura lateralis cerebri
11.	Middle temporal gyrus	Gyrus temporalis medius
12.	Superior temporal gyrus	Gyrus temporalis superior
13.	Superior temporal sulcus	Sulcus temporalis superior
14.	Opercular part of inferior frontal gyrus	Pars opercularis gyri frontalis inferioris
15.	Triangular part of inferior frontal gyrus	Pars triangularis gyri frontalis inferioris
16.	Orbital part of inferior frontal gyrus	Pars orbitalis gyri frontalis inferioris
17.	Anterior ascending limb of lateral fissure	Ramus anterior ascendens fissurae lateralis
18.	Inferior precentral sulcus	Sulcus precentralis inferior
19.	Middle frontal gyrus	Gyrus frontalis medius
20.	Superior frontal sulcus	Sulcus frontalis superior
21.	Superior frontal gyrus	Gyrus frontalis superior
22.	Precentral sulcus	Sulcus precentralis
23.	Precentral gyrus	Gyrus precentralis
24.	Central sulcus	Sulcus centralis

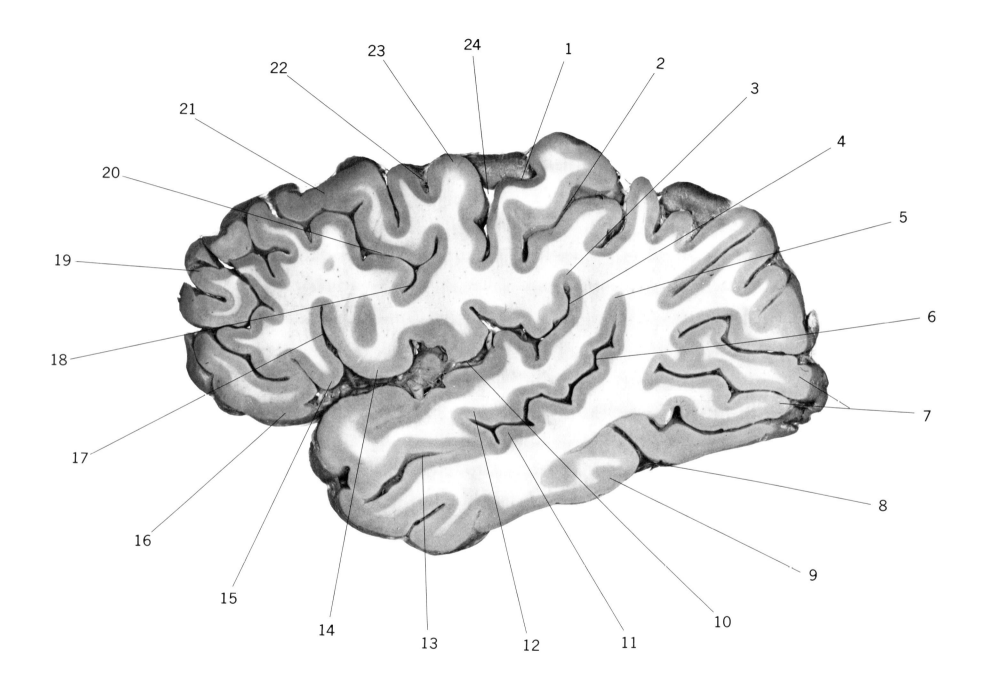

Lateral Surface of Sagittal Section through Insula X1.4

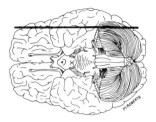

1.	Precentral operculum	Operculum precentrale
2.	Centrum semiovale	Centrum semiovale
3.	Parietal operculum	Operculum parietale
4.	Anterior transverse temporal gyrus	Gyrus temporalis transversus anterior
5.	Long gyrus of insula	Gyrus longus insulae
6.	Central fissure of insula	Fissura centralis insulae
7.	Occipital lobe	Lobus occipitalis
8.	Circular sulcus of insula	Sulcus circularis insulae
9.	White laminae of cerebellum	Laminae albae cerebelli
10.	Horizontal fissure	Fissura horizontalis
11.	Corpus medullare of cerebellum	Corpus medullare cerebelli
12.	Optic radiations	Radiatio optica
13.	Temporal operculum	Operculum temporale
14.	Precentral gyrus of insula	Gyrus precentralis insulae
15.	Middle cerebral artery	Arteria cerebri media
16.	Lateral cerebral fissure	Fissura lateralis cerebri
17.	Orbital operculum	Operculum orbitale
18.	Orbital gyri	Gyri orbitales
19.	Inferior frontal gyrus	Gyrus frontalis inferior
20.	Frontal lobe	Lobus frontalis
21.	Short gyri of insula	Gyri breves insulae
22.	Circular sulcus of insula	Sulcus circularis insulae
23.	Frontal operculum	Operculum frontale
24.	Inferior precentral sulcus	Sulcus precentralis inferior

64

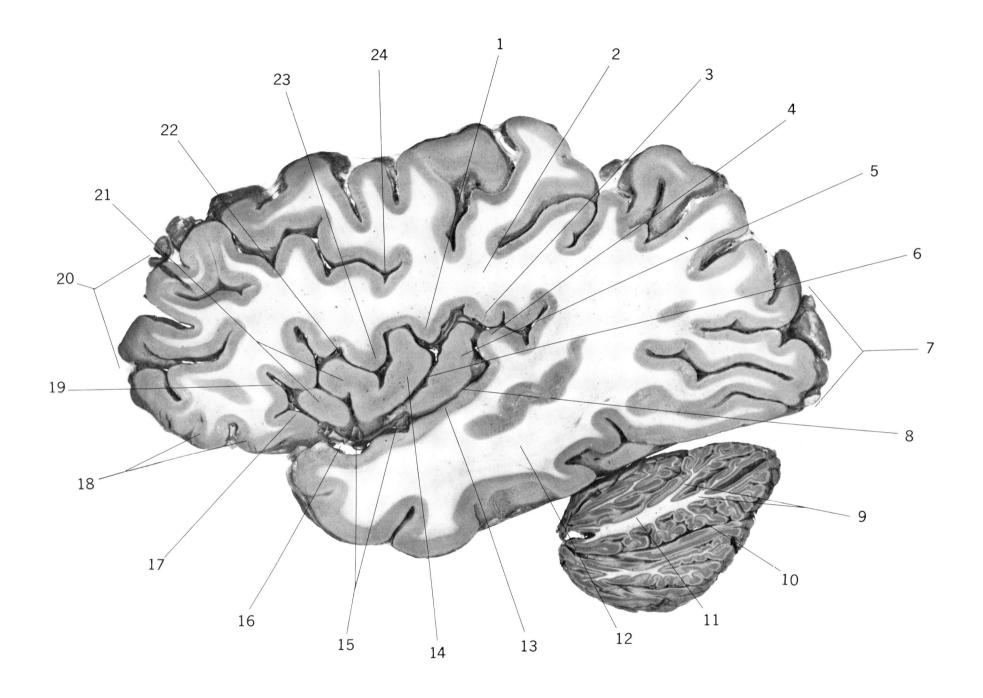

Lateral Surface of Sagittal Section through Claustrum and Lateral Limit of Putamen X1.4

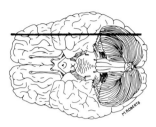

1.	Centrum semiovale	Centrum semiovale
2.	External capsule	Capsula externa
3.	Optic radiations	Radiatio optica
4.	Acoustic radiations	Radiatio acustica
5.	Tail of caudate nucleus	Cauda nuclei caudati
6.	Posterior horn of lateral ventricle	Cornu posterius ventriculi lateralis
7.	Occipital lobe	Lobus occipitalis
8.	Hippocampus	Hippocampus
9.	Horizontal fissure	Fissura horizontalis
10.	Corpus medullare of cerebellum	Corpus medullare cerebelli
11.	Lateral occipitotemporal gyrus	Gyrus occipitotemporalis lateralis
12.	Inferior horn of lateral ventricle	Cornu inferius ventriculi lateralis
13.	Amygdala	Corpus amygdaloideum
14.	Limen of insula	Limen insulae
15.	Middle cerebral artery	Arteria cerebri media
16.	Lateral cerebral fissure	Fissura lateralis cerebri
17.	Extreme capsule	Capsula extrema
18.	Orbital gyri	Gyri orbitales
19.	Frontal pole	Polus frontalis
20.	Inferior frontal gyrus	Gyrus frontalis inferior
21.	Insula	Insula
22.	Middle frontal gyrus	Gyrus frontalis medius
23.	Superior frontal gyrus	Gyrus frontalis superior
24.	Putamen	Putamen
25.	Claustrum	Claustrum

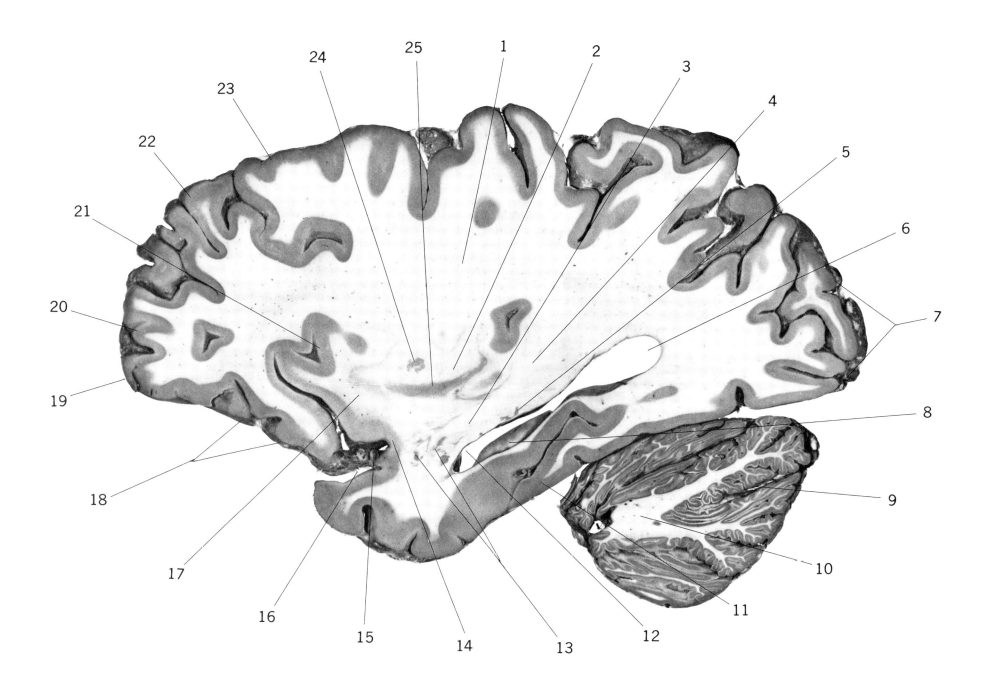

Medial Surface of Sagittal Section through
Lateral Portion of Putamen X1.4

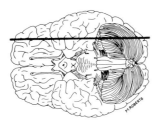

1.	Putamen	Putamen
2.	Sublenticular part of internal capsule	Pars sublenticularis capsulae internae
3.	Acoustic radiations	Radiatio acustica
4.	Retrolenticular part of internal capsule	Pars retrolenticularis capsulae internae
5.	Forceps major of corpus callosum	Forceps major corporis callosi
6.	Tail of caudate nucleus	Cauda nuclei caudati
7.	Optic radiations	Radiatio optica
8.	Posterior horn of lateral ventricle	Cornu posterius ventriculi lateralis
9.	Occipital gyri	Gyri occipitales
10.	Fimbria of hippocampus	Fimbria hippocampi
11.	Medial occipitotemporal gyrus	Gyrus occipitotemporalis medialis
12.	Optic radiations	Radiatio optica
13.	Corpus medullare of cerebellum	Corpus medullare cerebelli
14.	Hippocampus	Hippocampus
15.	Parahippocampal gyrus	Gyrus parahippocampalis
16.	Anterior commissure	Commissura anterior
17.	Cingulum	Cingulum
18.	Amygdala	Corpus amygdaloideum
19.	Uncinate fasciculus	Fasciculus uncinatus
20.	Middle cerebral artery	Arteria cerebri media
21.	Lateral cerebral fissure	Fissura lateralis cerebri
22.	Limen of insula	Limen insulae
23.	Claustrum	Claustrum
24.	Orbital gyri	Gyri orbitales
25.	Frontal pole	Polus frontalis
26.	Extreme capsule	Capsula extrema
27.	External capsule	Capsula externa
28.	Middle frontal gyrus	Gyrus frontalis medius
29.	Corona radiata	Corona radiata
30.	Putamen	Putamen
31.	Centrum semiovale	Centrum semiovale
32.	Corona radiata	Corona radiata

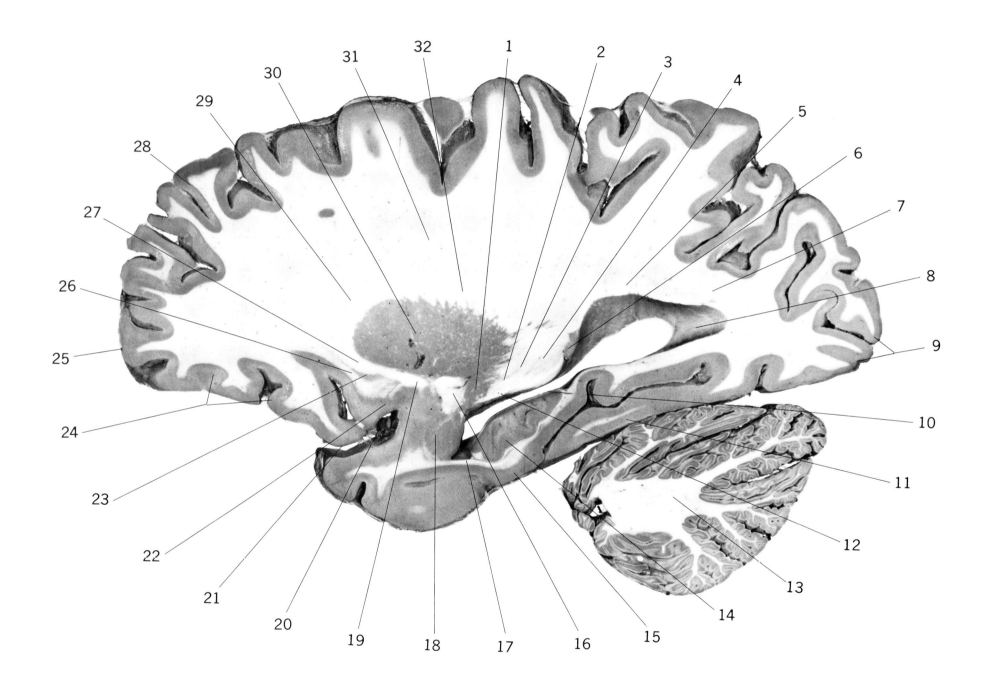

69

Lateral Surface of Sagittal Section through Termination of Optic Tract X1.4

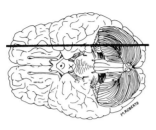

1. Acoustic radiations — Radiatio acustica
2. Tail of caudate nucleus — Cauda nuclei caudati
3. Stria terminalis — Stria terminalis
4. Choroid plexus — Plexus choroideus
5. Posterior horn of lateral ventricle — Cornu posterius ventriculi lateralis
6. Calcar avis — Calcar avis
7. Reticular nucleus of thalamus — Nucleus reticularis thalami
8. Medial occipitotemporal gyrus — Gyrus occipitotemporalis medialis
9. Choroidal fissure — Fissura choroidea
10. Optic radiations — Radiatio optica
11. Fimbria of hippocampus — Fimbria hippocampi
12. Lateral geniculate body — Corpus geniculatum laterale
13. Hippocampus — Hippocampus
14. Optic tract — Tractus opticus
15. Cingulum — Cingulum
16. Dentate gyrus — Gyrus dentatus
17. Inferior horn of lateral ventricle — Cornu inferius ventriculi laterali
18. Middle cerebral artery — Arteria cerebri media
19. Anterior commissure — Commissura anterior
20. Anterolateral lenticulostriate branches of middle cerebral artery — Rami lenticulostriati arteriae cerebralis mediae
21. External medullary lamina of globus pallidus — Lamina medullaris externa pallidi
22. Putamen — Putamen
23. Anterior limb of internal capsule — Crus anterius capsulae internae
24. Corona radiata — Corona radiata
25. Globus pallidus II — Globus pallidus II
26. Internal medullary lamina of globus pallidus — Lamina medullaris interna pallidi
27. Globus pallidus I — Globus pallidus I
28. Pregeniculate nucleus — Nucleus pregeniculatum

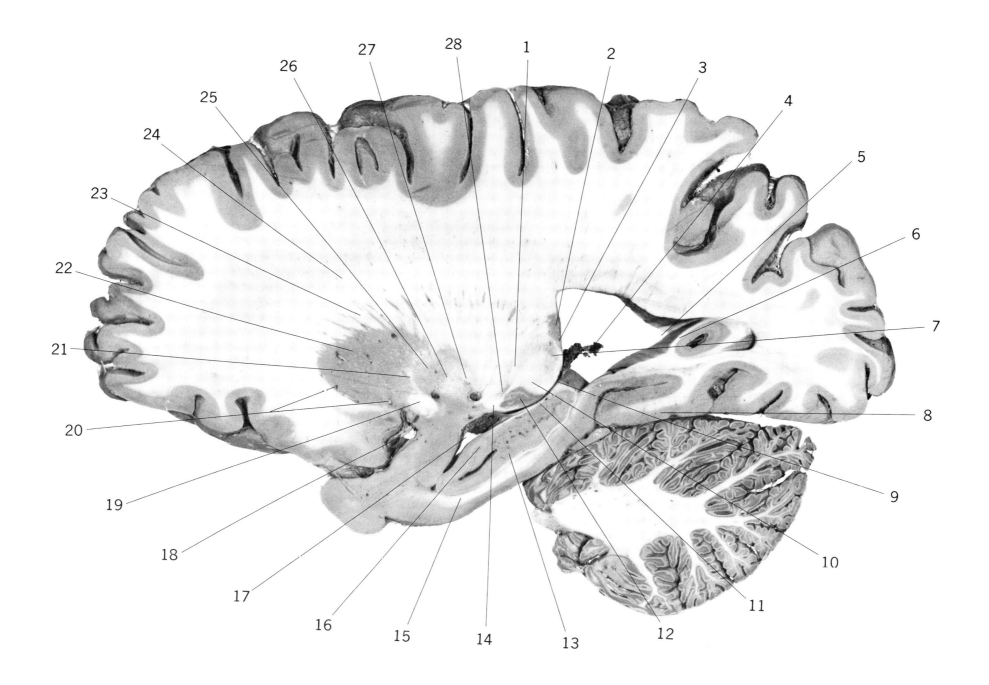

Lateral Surface of Sagittal Section through
Lateral Pulvinar Nucleus X1.4

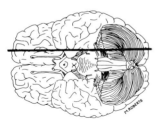

1.	Lateral pulvinar nucleus of thalamus	Nucleus pulvinaris lateralis thalami
2.	Choroidal fissure	Fissura choroidea
3.	Choroid plexus	Plexus choroideus
4.	Fimbria of hippocampus	Fimbria hippocampi
5.	Atrium of lateral ventricle	Atrium ventriculi lateralis
6.	Alveus of hippocampus	Alveus hippocampi
7.	Calcarine sulcus	Sulcus calcarinus
8.	Cingulum	Cingulum
9.	Lateral geniculate body	Corpus geniculatum laterale
10.	Cerebral peduncle	Pedunculus cerebri
11.	Optic tract	Tractus opticus
12.	Alveus of hippocampus	Alveus hippocampi
13.	Hippocampal sulcus	Sulcus hippocampi
14.	Vestibulocochlear nerve (VIII)	Nervus vestibulocochlearis (VIII)
15.	Trigeminal nerve (V)	Nervus trigeminus (V)
16.	Globus pallidus I	Globus pallidus I
17.	Amygdala	Corpus amygdaloideum
18.	Lateral olfactory stria	Stria olfactoria lateralis
19.	Anterior commissure	Commissura anterior
20.	Internal medullary lamina of globus pallidus	Lamina medullaris interna pallidi
21.	Putamen	Putamen
22.	External medullary lamina of globus pallidus	Lamina medullaris externa pallidi
23.	Globus pallidus II	Globus pallidus II
24.	Head of caudate nucleus	Caput nuclei caudati
25.	Transcapsular caudatolenticular gray striae	Striae griseae caudatolenticulares transcapsulares
26.	Anterior limb of internal capsule	Crus anterius capsulae internae
27.	Genu of internal capsule	Genu capsulae internae
28.	Pregeniculate nucleus	Nucleus pregeniculatum
29.	Centrum semiovale	Centrum semiovale
30.	Posterior lateral nucleus of thalamus	Nucleus lateralis posterior thalami
31.	Posterior limb of internal capsule	Crus posterius capsulae internae
32.	Triangular area	Area triangularis

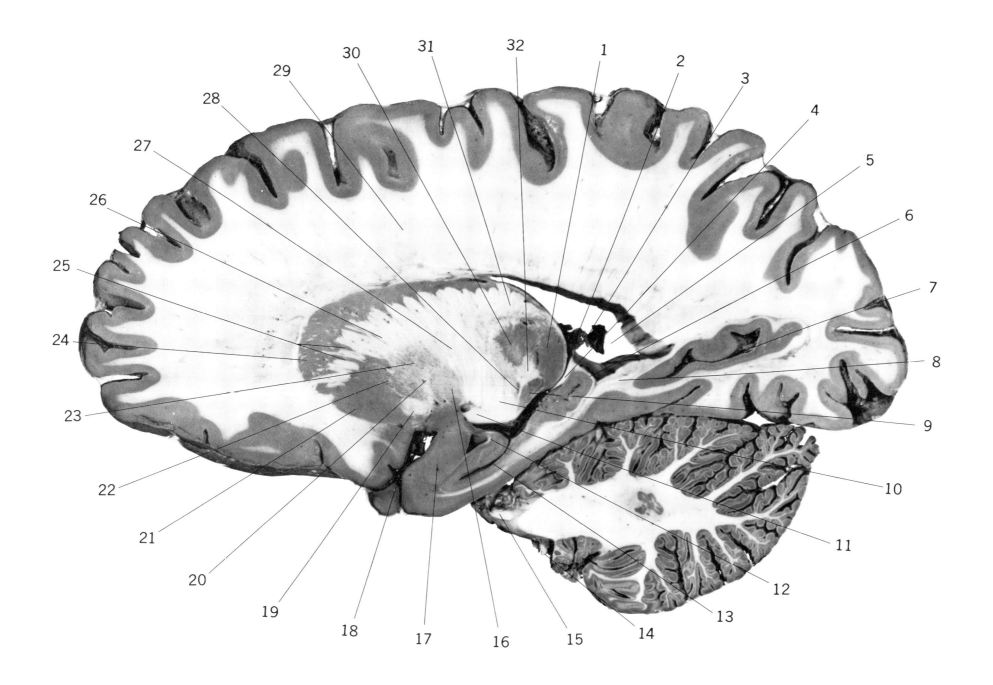

Lateral Surface of Sagittal Section through
Cisterna Ambiens X1.4

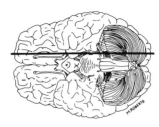

1.	Lateral ventral nucleus of thalamus	Nucleus ventralis lateralis thalami
2.	Posterolateral ventral nucleus of thalamus	Nucleus ventralis posterolateralis thalami
3.	Medial geniculate body	Corpus geniculatum mediale
4.	Medial pulvinar nucleus of thalamus	Nucleus pulvinaris medialis thalami
5.	Dentate gyrus	Gyrus dentatus
6.	Cingulum	Cingulum
7.	Optic radiations	Radiatio optica
8.	Calcarine sulcus	Sulcus calcarinus
9.	Parahippocampal gyrus	Gyrus parahippocampalis
10.	Semilunar lobule	Lobulus semilunaris
11.	Corpus medullare of cerebellum	Corpus medullare cerebelli
12.	Dentate nucleus	Nucleus dentatus
13.	Middle cerebellar peduncle	Pedunculus cerebellaris medius
14.	Lateral aperature of fourth ventricle	Apertura lateralis ventriculi quarti
15.	Cisterna ambiens	Cisterna ambiens
16.	Posterior cerebral artery	Arteria cerebri posterior
17.	Cerebral peduncle	Pedunculus cerebri
18.	Optic tract	Tractus opticus
19.	Middle cerebral artery	Arteria cerebri media
20.	Olfactory area	Area olfactoria
21.	Olfactory tubercle	Tuberculum olfactorium
22.	Orbital gyri	Gyri orbitales
23.	Putamen	Putamen
24.	Anterior commissure	Commissura anterior
25.	Globus pallidus	Globus pallidus
26.	Anterior horn of lateral ventricle	Cornu anterius ventriculi lateralis
27.	Head of caudate nucleus	Caput nuclei caudati
28.	Anterior limb of internal capsule	Crus anterius capsulae internae
29.	Genu of internal capsule	Genu capsulae internae
30.	Body of lateral ventricle	Corpus ventriculi lateralis
31.	Stratum zonale thalamus	Stratum zonale thalami
32.	Body of corpus callosum	Truncus corporis callosi

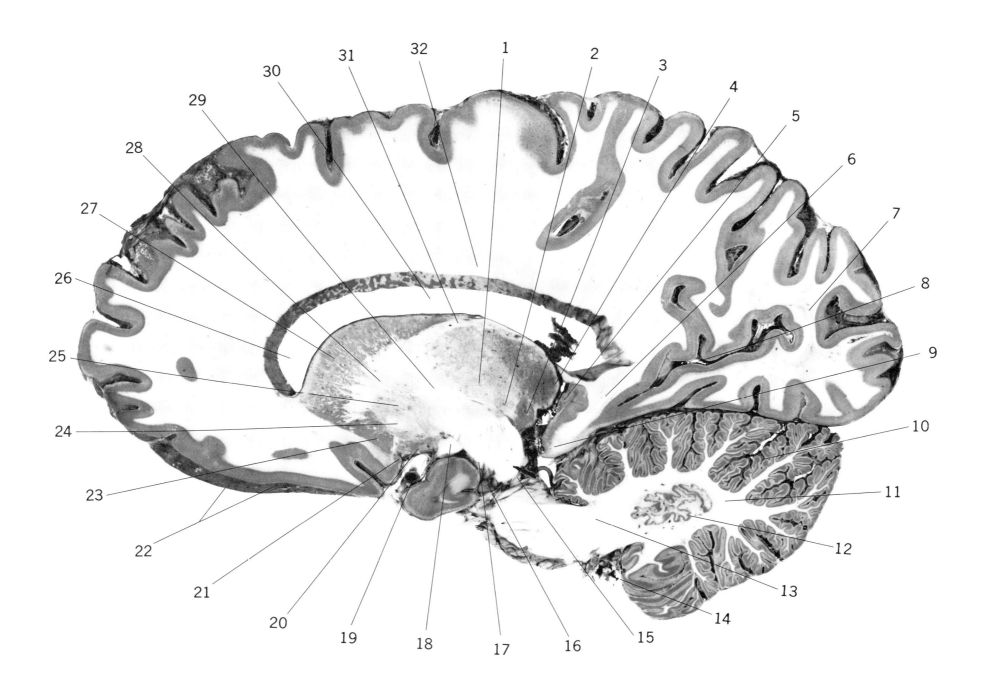

Medial Surface of Sagittal Section through Olfactory Tract X1.4

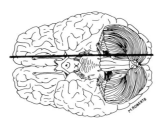

1.	Stratum zonale of thalamus	Stratum zonale thalami
2.	Centromedian nucleus of thalamus	Nucleus centromedianus thalami
3.	Posteromedial ventral nucleus of thalamus	Nucleus ventralis posteromedialis thalami
4.	Choroid plexus	Plexus choroideus
5.	Crus of fornix	Crus fornicis
6.	Medial pulvinar nucleus of thalamus	Nucleus pulvinaris medialis thalami
7.	Brachium of superior colliculus	Brachium colliculi superioris
8.	Subthalamicotegmental tract	Tractus subthalamicotegmentalis
9.	Medial lemniscus	Lemniscus medialis
10.	Posterior cerebral artery	Arteria cerebri posterior
11.	Peduncle of substantia nigra	Pedunculus substantiae nigrae
12.	Dentate nucleus	Nucleus dentatus
13.	Substantia nigra	Substantia nigra
14.	Inferior cerebellar peduncle	Pedunculus cerebellaris inferior
15.	Middle cerebellar peduncle	Pedunculus cerebellaris medius
16.	Pontine nuclei	Nuclei pontis
17.	Subthalamic nucleus	Nucleus subthalamicus
18.	Optic tract	Tractus opticus
19.	Ansa lenticularis	Ansa lenticularis
20.	Internal carotid artery	Arteria carotis interna
21.	Olfactory tract	Tractus olfactorius
22.	Putamen	Putamen
23.	Tegmental area H_2	Area tegmentalis H_2
24.	Anterior commissure	Commissura anterior
25.	Zona incerta	Zona incerta
26.	Anterior horn of lateral ventricle	Cornu anterius ventriculi lateralis
27.	Head of caudate nucleus	Caput nuclei caudati
28.	Anterior ventral nucleus of thalamus	Nucleus ventralis anterior thalami
29.	Lateral ventral nucleus of thalamus	Nucleus ventralis lateralis thalami
30.	Corpus callosum	Corpus callosum
31.	Lamina cornea and thalamostriate vein	Lamina cornea et vena thalamostriata
32.	Cerebellorubrothalamic tract	Tractus cerebellothalamicus

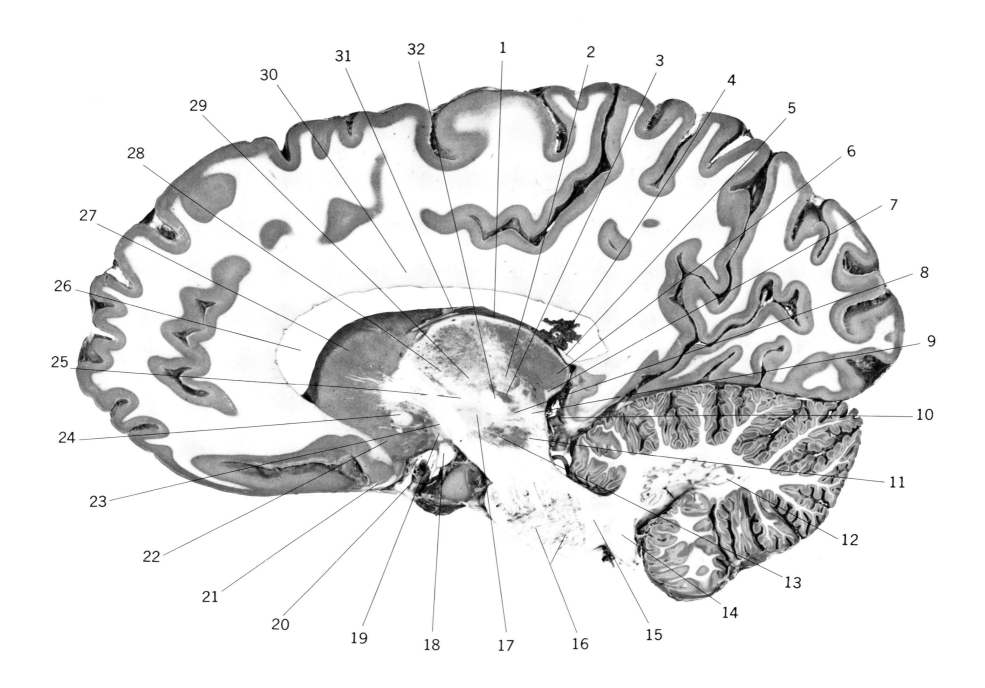

Lateral Surface of Sagittal Section through
Olfactory Tract X1.4

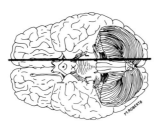

1.	Stratum zonale of thalamus	Stratum zonale thalami
2.	Centromedian nucleus of thalamus	Nucleus centromedianus thalami
3.	Posteromedial ventral nucleus of thalamus	Nucleus ventralis posteromedialis thalami
4.	Medial pulvinar nucleus of thalamus	Nucleus pulvinaris medialis thalami
5.	Medial geniculate body	Corpus geniculatum mediale
6.	Cingulum	Cingulum
7.	Parahippocampal gyrus	Gyrus parahippocampalis
8.	Medial lemniscus	Lemniscus medialis
9.	Peduncle of substantia nigra	Pedunculus substantiae nigrae
10.	Lateral corticobulbar fibers	Fibrae corticobulbares laterales
11.	Dentate nucleus	Nucleus dentatus
12.	Inferior cerebellar peduncle	Pedunculus cerebellaris inferior
13.	Pontine nuclei	Nuclei pontis
14.	Olive	Oliva
15.	Abducens nerve (VI)	Nervus abducens (VI)
16.	Substantia nigra	Substantia nigra
17.	Subthalamicotegemental tract	Tractus subthalamicotegementalis
18.	Posterior cerebral artery	Arteria cerebri posterior
19.	Uncus	Uncus
20.	Oculomotor nerve (III)	Nervus oculomotorius (III)
21.	Optic nerve (II)	Nervus opticus (II)
22.	Olfactory tract	Tractus olfactorius
23.	Anterior cerebral artery	Arteria cerebri anterior
24.	Capsule of subthalamic nucleus	Capsula nuclei subthalamici
25.	Subthalamic nucleus	Nucleus subthalamicus
26.	Anterior limb of internal capsule	Crus anterius capsulae internae
27.	Head of caudate nucleus	Caput nuclei caudati
28.	Genu of internal capsule	Genu capaulae internae
29.	Tegmental area H_2	Area tegmentalis H_2
30.	Tegmental area H_1	Area tegmentalis H_1
31.	Zona inserta	Zona incerta
32.	Posterior lateral nucleus of thalamus	Nucleus lateralis posterior thalami

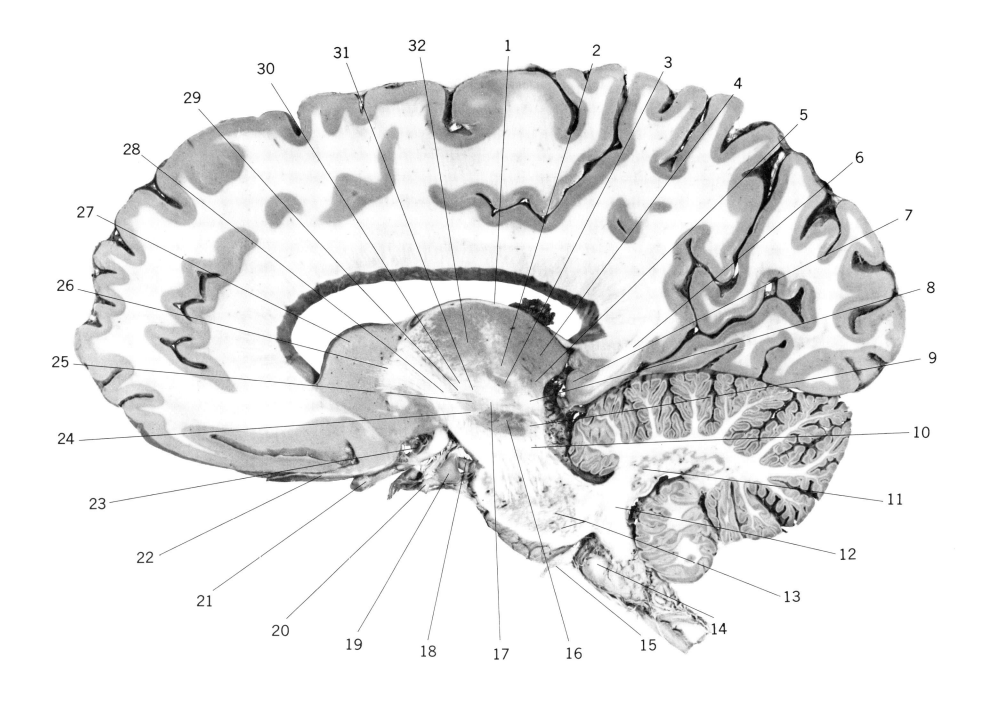

Medial Surface of Sagittal Section through Superior Cerebellar Peduncle X1.4

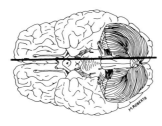

1.	Prerubral tract	Tractus prerubralis
2.	Dorsal medial nucleus of thalamus	Nucleus medialis dorsalis thalami
3.	Crus of fornix	Crus fornicis
4.	Medial pulvinar nucleus of thalamus	Nucleus pulvinaris medialis thalami
5.	Pretectal area	Area pretectalis
6.	Fasciolar gyrus	Gyrus fasciolaris
7.	Posterior cerebral artery	Arteria cerebri posterior
8.	Calcarine sulcus	Sulcus calcarinus
9.	Medial lemniscus	Lemniscus medialis
10.	Lateral lemniscus	Lemniscus lateralis
11.	Superior cerebellar peduncle	Pedunculus cerebellaris superior
12.	Dentate nucleus	Nucleus dentatus
13.	Striae medullares of fourth ventricle	Striae medullares ventriculi quarti
14.	Medial lemniscus	Lemniscus medialis
15.	Corticospinal tract	Tractus corticospinalis
16.	Abducens nerva (VI)	Nervus abducens (VI)
17.	Substantia nigra	Substantia nigra
18.	Medullary lamina of red nucleus	Lamina medullaris nuclei rubris
19.	Posterior cerebral artery	Arteria cerebri posterior
20.	Tegmental area H	Area tegmentalis H
21.	Optic nerve (II)	Nervus opticus (II)
22.	Ansa lenticularis	Ansa lenticularis
23.	Tegmental area H_2	Area tegmentalis H_2
24.	Inferior thalamic peduncle	Pedunculus thalami inferior
25.	Zona incerta	Zona incerta
26.	Tegmental area H_1	Area tegmentalis H_1
27.	Ventricular surface of head of caudate nucleus	Caput nuclei caudati
28.	Mamillothalamic fasciculus	Fasciculus mamillothalamicus
29.	Cingulate sulcus	Sulcus cinguli
30.	Anteroventral nucleus of thalamus	Nucleus anteroventralis thalami
31.	Posteromedial ventral nucleus of thalamus	Nucleus ventralis posteromedialis thalami
32.	Internal medullary lamina of thalamus	Lamina medullaris interna thalami

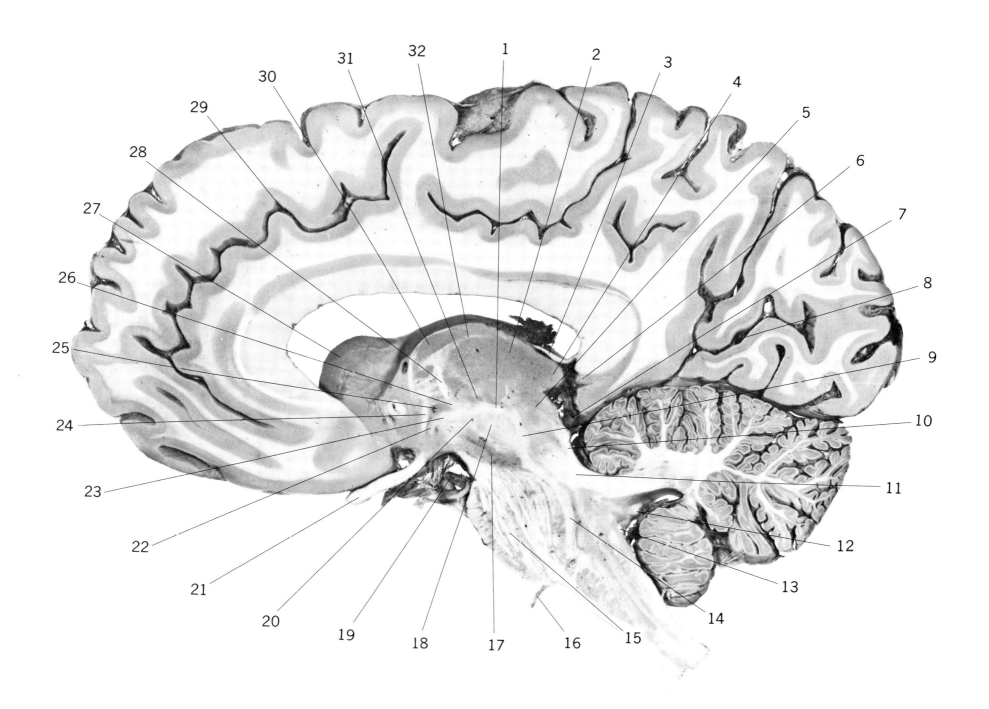

Medial Surface of Sagittal Section through Medial Extent of Red Nucleus X1.4

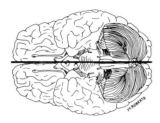

1.	Choroid plexus of lateral ventricle	Plexus choroideus ventriculi lateralis
2.	Central sulcus	Sulcus centralis
3.	Marginal branch of cingulate sulcus	Ramus marginalis sulci cingulati
4.	Precuneus	Precuneus
5.	Body of fornix	Corpus fornicis
6.	Parietooccipital sulcus	Sulcus parietooccipitalis
7.	Cuneus	Cuneus
8.	Calcarine sulcus	Sulcus calcarinus
9.	Lingual gyrus	Gyrus lingualis
10.	Pineal gland	Corpus pineale
11.	Superior and inferior colliculi	Colliculi, superior et inferior
12.	Fastidial nucleus	Nucleus fastigii
13.	Decussation of trochlear nerve (IV)	Decussatio nervorum trochlearium
14.	Fourth ventricle	Ventriculus quartus
15.	Red nucleus	Nucleus ruber
16.	Medial arcuate nucleus	Nucleus arcuatus medialis
17.	Fasciculus retroflexus	Fasciculus retroflexus
18.	Superficial pontine stratum	Stratum superficiale pontis
19.	Principal mamillary fasciculus	Fasciculus mamillaris princeps
20.	Infundibulm	Infundibulum
21.	Optic chiasm	Chiasma opticum
22.	Anterior cerebral artery	Arteria cerebri anterior
23.	Straight gyrus	Gyrus rectus
24.	Parolfactory area	Area parolfactoria
25.	Anterior commissure	Commissura anterior
26.	Column of fornix	Columna fornicis
27.	Genu of corpus callosum	Genu corporis callosi
28.	Stria medullaris of thalamus	Stria medullaris thalami
29.	Anteromedial nucleus of thalamus	Nucleus anteromedialis thalami
30.	Cingulate sulcus	Sulcus cinguli
31.	Sulcus of corpus callosum	Sulcus corporis callosi
32.	Cingulum	Cingulum
33.	Cingulate gyrus	Gyrus cinguli
34.	Dorsal medial nucleus of thalamus	Nucleus medialis dorsalis thalami
35.	Body of corpus callosum	Truncus corporis callosi
36.	Precentral sulcus	Sulcus precentralis

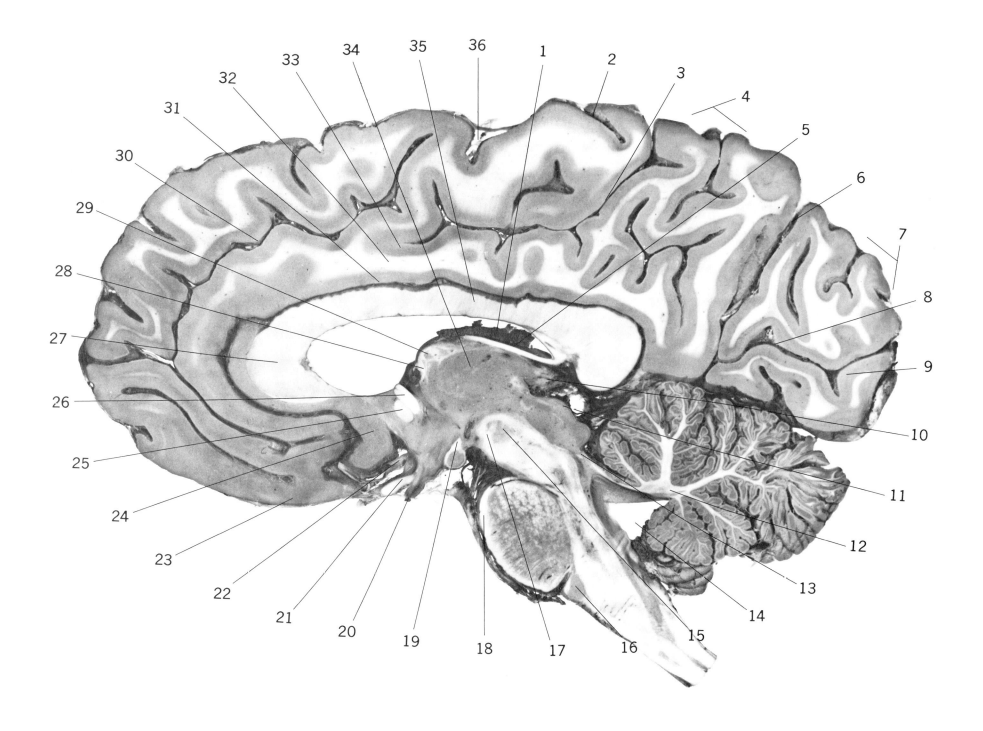

Medial Surface of Sagittal Section through Cerebral Aqueduct X1.4

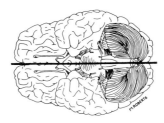

1.	Stria medullaris of thalamus	Stria medullaris thalami
2.	Third ventricle	Ventriculus tertius
3.	Habenular commissure	Commissura habenularum
4.	Pineal gland	Corpus pineale
5.	Stratum opticum	Stratum opticum
6.	Cerebral aqueduct	Aqueductus cerebri
7.	Inferior colliculus	Colliculus inferior
8.	Central gray substance	Stratum griseum centrale
9.	Superior medullary velum	Velum medullare superius
10.	Decussation of superior cerebellar peduncle	Decussatio pedunculorum cerebellarium superiorum
11.	Medial longitudinal fasciculus	Fasciculus longitudinalis medialis
12.	Superior central nucleus	Nucleus centralis superior
13.	Choroid plexus of fourth ventricle	Plexus choroideus ventriculi quarti
14.	Obex	Obex
15.	Inferior central nucleus	Nucleus centralis inferior
16.	Medulla oblongata	Medulla oblongata
17.	Posterior commissure	Commissura posterior
18.	Interpeduncular nucleus	Nucleus interpeduncularis
19.	Basilar artery	Arteria basilaris
20.	Central rami of basilar artery	Arteria basilaris, rami centrales
21.	Posterior perforated substance	Substantia perforata posterior
22.	Mamillary body	Corpus mamillare
23.	Infundibular recess	Recessus infundibuli
24.	Supraoptic recess	Recessus supraopticus
25.	Lamina terminalis	Lamina terminalis
26.	Hypothalamus	Hypothalamus
27.	Preoptic area	Area preoptica
28.	Pericallosal artery	Arteria pericallosa
29.	Anterior commissure	Commissura anterior
30.	Septum pellucidum	Septum pellucidum
31.	Interventricular foramen	Foramen interventriculae
32.	Column of fornix	Columna fornicis
33.	Paraventricular nucleus of thalamus	Nucleus paraventricularis thalami
34.	Body of fornix	Corpus fornicis
35.	Arachnoidal granulations	Granulationes arachnoideales
36.	Velum interpositum and tela choroidea	Velum interpositum et tela choroidea

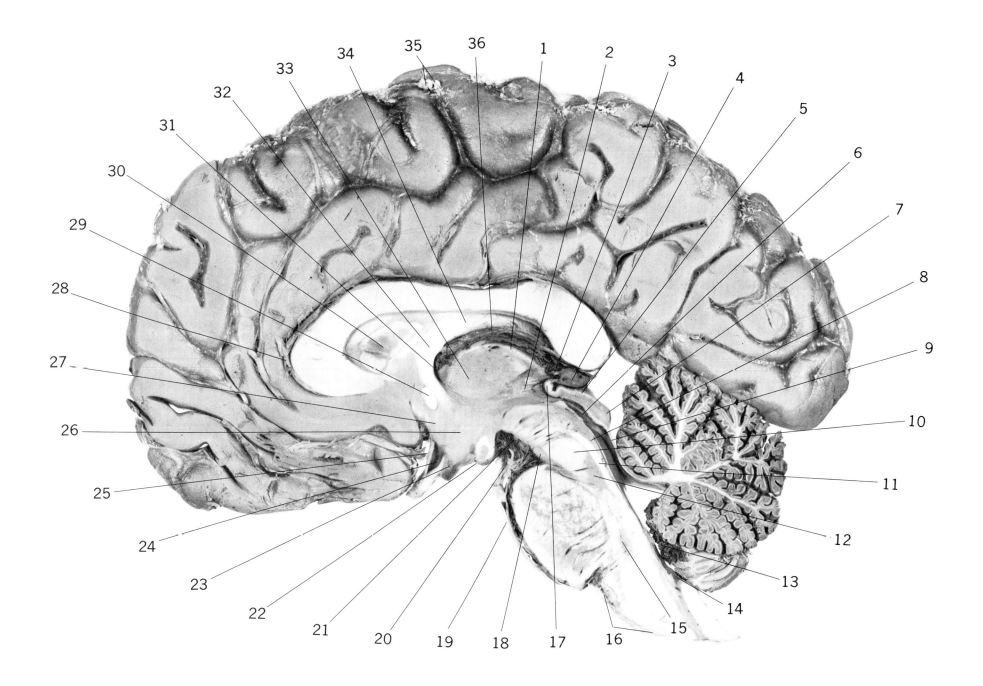

85

INDEX

Gyrus(i) (*Continued*)

occipitales, 62, 68

occipitotemporalis lateralis, 14, 16, 20, 24, 26, 30, 32, 34, 66

occipitotemporalis medialis, 68, 70

orbitales, 2, 4, 64, 66, 68, 74

orbitalis medialis, 2, 56, 58

parahippocampalis, 14, 16, 20, 24, 26, 58, 68, 74, 78

parietalis inferior, 34

parietalis medialis, 38, 40

parietalis superior, 34

postcentralis, 16, 20, 30, 38, 40, 62

precentralis, 16, 30, 38, 62

precentralis insulae, 44, 48, 64

rectus, 2, 4, 6, 56, 58, 82

retrospleniales hippocampi, 30, 50

supramarginalis, 62

temporalis inferior, 6, 14, 16, 24, 26, 32, 34, 62

temporalis medius, 4, 6, 14, 26, 30, 34, 54, 62

temporalis superior, 4, 6, 14, 16, 24, 26, 34, 54, 62

temporalis transversus anterior, 64

H FIELD of Forel. See *Tegmental area H.*

H₁ field of Forel. See *Tegmental area H₁.*

H₂ field of Forel. See *Tegmental area H₂.*

Habenular commissure, 52, 84

Habenulointerpeduncular tract. See *Fasciculus retroflexus.*

Head of caudate nucleus, 4, 6, 8, 10, 12, 38, 40, 42, 44, 46, 48, 50, 52, 54, 72, 74, 76, 78, 80

Hippocampal

commissure. See *Commissure of fornix.*

sulcus, 18, 20, 30, 72

Hippocampus, 14, 18, 20, 22, 26, 28, 30, 32, 52, 56, 58, 66, 68, 70

Horizontal fissure, 34, 64, 66

Hypoglossal trigone, 30

Hypothalamus, 20, 84

INCISURA preoccipitalis, 62

Incomplete medullary lamina of globus pallidus, 14

Indusium griseum, 32, 40

Inferior

central nucleus (of Roller), 84

cerebellar decussation, 34

peduncle, 28, 76, 78

colliculus, 28, 30, 58, 82, 84

frontal gyrus, 2, 4, 6, 10, 14, 64, 66

frontal sulcus, 2, 6, 10

horn of lateral ventricle, 16, 18, 24, 26, 28, 32, 56, 66, 70

Inferior (*Continued*)

longitudinal fasciculus, 28, 30, 32, 52

occipitofrontal fasciculus, 2, 8

olivary nucleus, 24, 26

parietal gyrus, 34

parietal lobule, 30

precentral sulcus, 62, 64

temporal gyrus, 6, 14, 16, 24, 26, 32, 34, 62

temporal sulcus, 6, 34

thalamic peduncle, 80

Infundibular recess, 84

Infundibulum, 10, 58, 82

Insula, 8, 12, 40, 42, 66

Internal

carotid artery, 8, 76

cerebral vein, 28, 32, 46

medullary lamina of globus pallidus, 10, 12, 14, 18, 50, 52, 70, 72

medullary lamina of thalamus, 14, 20, 42, 44, 80

Interpeduncular

fossa, 18, 20, 22, 58

nucleus, 22, 84

Interthalamic adhesion, 14, 18, 50

Interventricular foramen (of Monro), 12, 84

Intracerebral anastomatic veins, 2

Intraparietal sulcus, 34, 38, 40

Island of Reil. See *Insula.*

LAMINA(E)

albae cerebelli, 34, 64

cornea, 76

medullaris externa pallidi, 8, 10, 14, 18, 48, 50, 52, 70, 72

medullaris externa thalami, 12, 16, 26

medullaris incompleta pallidi, 14

medullaris interna pallidi, 10, 12, 14, 18, 50, 52, 70, 72

medullaris interna thalami, 14, 20, 42, 44, 46, 80

medullaris nuclei rubris, 22, 80

of septum pellucidum, 4, 42, 44

septi pellucidi, 4, 42, 44

terminalis, 84

Lateral

aperature of fourth ventricle (of Luschka), 74

cerebral fissure (of Sylvius), 4, 8, 10, 26, 38, 40, 50, 56, 62, 64, 66, 68

corticobulbar fibers, 78

dorsal nucleus of thalamus, 22, 42, 44

geniculate body, 24, 54, 56, 70, 72

habenular nucleus, 52

lemniscus, 24, 26, 58, 80